FROM SOFA TO START LINE

www.tismenterprises.com

FROM SOFA TO START LINE

HOW I LOST 15 STONE & STARTED RUNNING MARATHONS

MIKE HARE

THE INCREDIBLE SHRINKING MAN

PUBLISHED BY TISM ENTERPRISES LIMITED
33 Admiral House, Viersen Platz, Peterborough PE1 1ES
www.tismenterprises.com

ISBN 978-0-9562479-0-2

The publishers have made every effort to contact those persons having rights in any of the photographs reproduced here. Where this has not been possible, the publishers will be pleased to hear from anyone who recognises their work, and will make every endeavour to provide credits in subsequent editions.

Design by Julia Lloyd
Printed in Great Britain by the MPG Books Group, Bodmin and King's Lynn

2 4 6 8 10 9 7 5 3 1

To Gayle, Rosalind, Natalie and Veronica

(Number One, Number Two, Number Three and Number Four),
all together a unique demonstration of the diversity of perfection.

ACKNOWLEDGEMENTS

I PARTICULARLY WANT TO OFFER MY GRATITUDE AND SPECIAL THANKS TO A small number of wonderful people who have collectively provided me with the inspiration and support to achieve the transition to what I am today.

Para Handy, who said "Big Jim's using some tablets from his Doc, why don't you have a word with your doc?"And later said "Oh my god, it's The Incredible Shrinking Man". Also my best mate, my long time co-conspirator, my lifebelt in stormy seas, and to whom I have had to promise that I will never write THAT book!

Doctor Ken Rigg, of the Deepings Health Centre, who said "Yes, I'll help you, if you seriously want to lose some weight."And later said "I think it's time you did a run."

Mr Malata, Consultant in Reconstructive Surgery at Addenbrookes Hospital who said "Yes, we can remove all that loose skin"and later said "Why don't we do your thighs as well."

Mr Gillespie, Consultant in Reconstructive Surgery at Addenbrookes Hospital who said "You are OK to start to run again" and later said "There's nothing more we can do for you. It's remarkable."

Auld Thai Tam, who said "I'll bring a large jar to the Great North Run so we've got something to scrape you off the road into."

The Poseur, whose own battle inspired all my fund raising efforts for The Prostate Cancer Charity. A survivor, a gentleman, a pretty good driver, and the best kitty holder you could ever hope for!

The Auld Git, who said "I've never been to Athens. Can we come too?"

The Realbuzz bloggers, too numerous to mention by name (and I'm afraid I might inadvertently miss one or two). My 'running family', who have freely offered me their support, knowledge, advice and friendship, and welcomed me into their midst without reservation. They can have no real concept of just how much they mean to me, and their contribution to my becoming 'a marathon runner'. I will, however, specially mention Kitten, Martin H, Runningbee, Laurajehane, Man in the Stand and Russell Nimbus who all left comments on my first couple of blogs in March 2007 and with whom I have since run numerous races.

Finally to the Ladies of 'TEAM TISM'.

Sue Blake, without whose belief, dedication, knowledge and unwavering support this book would never have been written.

Leda Sammarco, whose guiding hand and light editorial touch have kept my ramblings in some sort of order.

Julia Lloyd – last, but by no means least – for having the immense talent required to actually make this all look good.

FOREWORD

ALTHOUGH IT MIGHT SEEM LIKE THE PATHWAY OF AN ELITE MARATHON runner and a 27.5 stone, highly stressed, inactive businessman have very little in common, in reality the personal journeys that each of us have travelled to reach our health and performance summits contain some remarkable similarities. Mike's journey resonates strongly with me because it clearly demonstrates his ability and willingness to step outside of what he'd previously thought possible and take positive action towards achieving dreams. His qualities of determination, patience, discipline, hard work and unfaltering commitment are the same as those required to win medals and compete at the highest levels of world sport. We're both marathoners and I count Mike as a runner just like me, it's just our quest to complete 26.2 miles has different meaning, objectives and outcomes.

Mike's journey starts with a car accident, too much time in the office, way too many extra puddings and ends with his remarkable change in body shape, a 15 stone weight loss and transition into a 'real authentic marathon runner'. It is an open, frank and honest account of the challenges he faces mentally, physically and emotionally as he embarks upon and completes the Athens Marathon.

Mike's story is a truly inspiring one that strikes right at the heart of a 'can do attitude'. As an athlete physical limits and boundaries simply don't exist. Mental and physical barriers are there to be cracked, attacked and overcome. Not in a particularly aggressive or confrontational way but in a way that brings real personal fulfillment, reward and satisfaction. This is true regardless of ability, talent or target and Mike demonstrates the ways in which his own weight loss and marathon running goals represented a journey for him of Olympic proportions. He provides clear examples of the ways in which he set himself clear and realistic goals that will have meaning and relativity for many readers.

Real change doesn't take place in a climate of comfort and neither does personal improvement. In this book Mike regularly steps out of his comfort zones and shows others how he achieves this. He makes it have meaning and seem real for others to do the same.

In the Beijing Olympic Games I arrived at the start line in the best shape of my life. I'd run personal bests all year including a 2.28 marathon clocking earlier in the year at the London Marathon. I felt this was my time. I confidently led the race for the first 10miles and waited for the pace to really kick in. Just before it did my race literally hit a major stumbling block as I was tripped and hit the Beijing tarmac with crashing impact. Bruised and battered and with what I later found out was a fractured rib my game plan changed. It was now about finishing, getting my head down and hurting my body and my pride and aiming for completion. Finishing in the Bird's Nest stadium wasn't quite as I'd imagined but giving up simply wasn't an option. The road to personal success is rarely smooth and frequently peppered with falls and setbacks. What matters most is the action you take when you fall and as Mike so capably demonstrates time and time again getting up, getting going, keeping going, time and time again brings results.

> "I did not die in the car crash. I should, perhaps, have died in the car crash. If so, this was, currently, a second chance. If I was to be given a second chance, then for heaven's sake, make better use of it"

I challenge you to read Mike's story of his own Olympic journey and not believe that you have the potential inside you to accomplish something that you've previously pushed to the back of your mind and thought ridiculous and out of your reach. Don't wait for a trigger moment or a second chance to force your hand. Take a personal lead. Find the way forward that works for you. Hold your head high in pursuit of your dreams and never, ever give up.

Liz Yelling

Commonwealth marathon medalist, two times Olympian and British Champion

I HAVE WORKED AS A GENERAL PRACTITIONER FOR 23 YEARS. IN THAT TIME I have had the fortune of helping people deal with all manner of life's challenging problems. A particularly difficult area is in helping people change their behaviour or lifestyle in order to improve their health. People find it hard to change their ways. Mike Hare's story is an extraordinary tale of dedication, hard work and total commitment to change. He came along following "a shock to the system" and adapted a new way of living with a zeal seldom seen. His account of the changes he has made is an open, honest, revealing story of the rollercoaster of emotions he faced in becoming "The Incredible Shrinking Man". Along the way he has developed a following, especially from documenting his progress online. He has helped many along the way and has become a true inspiration to all.

DR K. S. RIGG

ONE MAN DIES EVERY HOUR OF PROSTATE CANCER IN THE UK, WHICH IS something that Mike Hare is more than aware of, after losing three of his closest friends to the disease.

Mike's commitment to The Prostate Cancer Charity has been outstanding and it has been incredible to see the personal journey that he has taken over the years.

He has become one of the Charity's most loyal and vocal supporters, both by raising awareness of the disease and by generating much needed funding through his participation in countless events.

Mike's partnership with The Prostate Cancer Charity began in 2007 after he shed an impressive 15 stone to take part in the Great North Run. Since then, he has not stopped going the extra mile to help the Charity battle the disease.

All of the team at The Prostate Cancer Charity are hugely grateful for the amazing support that Mike has shown and wish him every success with his future activities.

JOHN NEATE
Chief Executive

FROM SOFA TO START LINE

CHAPTER ONE

CRASH & BURN

SOMETHING WAKES ME FROM MY BRIEF NAP. THERE ARE STRANGE RED DOTS in front of my eyes.

What are they? Oh, they're brake lights.

BRAKE LIGHTS! I'll never stop in time.

Go left? No, there are trees and water. Turn right, the road seems clear.

I swerve right and brake.

Shit – it's a bend. Something big is coming straight at me.

CRUNCH. Then, silence.

When I open my eyes this time, there are no red dots, just a grey foggy haze.

What is it? Oh, it's smoke.

SMOKE! GET OUT! Can't move, can't open the door, can't release seat belt.

Smoke means fire. Get out.

I CAN'T.

I swear my feet are getting hotter. Oh no, I've had it here.

My girls! Sorry girls. Oh GOD, what a way to go. GET OUT. I CAN'T. Oh, ssshhhiiittt!

This is going to hurt, really hurt.

IT'S TRUE WHAT THEY SAY. YOUR LIFE DOES FLASH BEFORE YOU IN THOSE few seconds before...

I'd arrived at this crunch point following a 50 year journey just going along with what life threw at me. After school I spent a couple of decades clambering up corporate ladders and chasing the salary cheque each month until redundancy at 40 catapulted me into the world of self-employment. Certainly I had played the game by all the normal rules. Married young, I spent some time out of the country working in the Channel Islands, managed to produce four gorgeous daughters, and had been lucky with the housing market at each move. But by this time all that mattered was being able to earn enough to keep the house going and provide for my girls.

Life had sneaked past me in recent years, and the last person on any list of priorities was me. I ended up running my own business and got caught up in helping another one to the extent that I would often work from 9 in the morning till midnight, with breaks in between to pop home and cater for the family. Having four girls and living in a rural town meant that *taxi driving* was often on the agenda as well.

I'd always been a *big lad*, played as a forward in the school rugby team, and then briefly for the local rugby club when I left school. I had never taken much notice of my weight, but for some strange reason I have always had a memory of being 12 stone 12lbs sometime during senior school. I have no recollection of when I was weighed, or why I was weighed, just this figure of 12:12 stuck in the back of the mind. For a couple of years after leaving school I had played a bit of sport, always getting involved in the works team for any local league be it 5-a-side, volleyball, table tennis. You name it; I would make up the numbers. It was not completely unknown for me to enter fully into the after match socialising either.

But then I spent some time helping to run a youth club, and the sports side began to fall away. Along came daughter number one, and with my other half working shifts at the local hospital I threw myself into the deep and abiding joys of bringing up the family. Perhaps, now that I start to reflect on the course that life has taken, it was at this point that I said goodbye to my sense of self, and drifted without conscious decision into the surprisingly satisfying role of servitude that is fatherhood.

I've always had a strong belief in doing what I can to help anyone wherever my skills or experience may be of benefit. It's probably a product of being brought up in the fifties and sixties in a home where Christian principles ruled day and night without question. So it came completely naturally to me to give up anything remotely selfish where the needs of family were concerned.

Daughter number two came along a short while later, and I took the chance to upgrade to a better job. By now virtually all participation in any sporting activities had ceased, but I got the chance to get a bit of exercise through gardening and occasional DIY. A couple of years later with my third daughter on the way, I felt it was time to move on from the insular environment of Guernsey and get back home to England. In the autumn of 1986 we moved to Hertfordshire, where I had been offered the chance to become the managing director of a brand new division being launched by a company based in the area. It was going to be a fascinating challenge introducing a new product to the national sales force, but I also had to endure a 60 mile roundtrip on the A1, daily.

The new job involved not only long hours setting up the new division, establishing the systems, and recruiting the administration staff, but trips all over the country running seminars and making presentations to the main company's existing field sales force. At the same time, the girls were starting off their school lives, and the house and garden needed knocking into shape. It was around this time that I first became vaguely aware that my shape was not quite what it used to be and that I no longer looked good in swimming trunks! I vaguely recall having a crack at a diet, but it interfered with the ability to do the corporate entertaining things, and rapidly got left on the shelf. But in your thirties, with a good job, a wife, three lovely daughters and a nice house you really don't spend time thinking about what may be waiting for you further down the road.

Three years later another change of job led to a very senior position in one of the largest and most established insurance companies in London. Even though this was at the very end of the eighties, the company still served its senior employees a three course lunch every day, with a drink from the bar as an aperitif. Not only that, but I was very quickly advised that it was virtually compulsory to attend, as it was, they told me, "an important forum for exchanging ideas between different departments at a senior level". Not one to rock the boat, I did as I was bidden, but the combination of trying to eat with the family every night was pretty disastrous, in retrospect.

The company then relocated to Peterborough, so we did too. We avoided the new houses being built around the new business park, and bought an old place in an outlying village next to a river. The kids loved it, and before long our fourth and final daughter was with us. But within a few short years the company was taken over, and I found myself redundant as the new owners brought in their own top people and started to re-shape the company's strategic direction. In fact on reflection, I believe it was not called redundancy, but outplacement (although I have personally never understood this particular piece of corporate jargon). My whole industry was in a state of flux, and I rapidly discovered that while no one was employing top personnel at that time, lots of the competitors were keen to take advantage of my experience and I decided to set up my own company. And this is where it all started to go pear-shaped (quite literally, as far as my body was concerned!).

I had four daughters, the oldest rapidly approaching university, a massive mortgage and a wife who felt that spending money, at the same rate as when I was on a corporate salary and expenses, was a God-given right. When I wasn't spending time ferrying my girls around I felt that I had to be working or I simply wasn't doing my best. I couldn't possibly take two weeks off for a holiday, what if a client wanted something? Food became whatever was to hand and quick, or otherwise it was wasting time. To make matters worse, most of my clients came from the industry where I had been employed, and still saw me in the same light as when I was on the *inside*, so a degree of excessive entertaining, be it on their budget or mine, was still a basic expectation.

For the last few years, this became a downward spiral. I worked hard to keep my girls grounded and spent as much time with them as possible. I had always been the one who read to them at night or helped them with their homework. If a good meal needed cooking, I cooked it. In fact my Christmas lunches, complete with handmade stuffing from an old recipe I was given by my mother-in-law, became a legend in the family. By now my wife had virtually withdrawn from social events, always having some excuse not to attend, and was taking less and less interest in the fundamentals of everyday parenthood.

Without realising it, I had totally lost all focus on me. I had not weighed myself for years, probably for fear of what I might find out, and as long as I didn't know the details, I wouldn't have to deal with it directly. I fell into a routine of getting the girls off to school, going to work, popping home for dinner around half past six and then going back to work until around midnight. I had got to the stage where I would actually use the car to go to work, even though my office was only about 300 yards from home. My excuse was that I might need to shoot off somewhere quickly and it would save time if the car was handy, plus it wasn't a good idea to be walking home through the town centre late at night.

This all led to a tendency to fall asleep during the day, which wasn't so bad if it was just me at my desk. However, when it happened, a couple of times, during staff meetings, the excuse that I was just *zoning out* to think an idea through, rapidly wore a bit thin. It is still something of a standing joke at my local Rotary Club that I could be virtually guaranteed to doze off during a meal, especially if a glass of red wine was involved. But at least it was just a bit of fun, they all knew me for the way I had brought my daughters up, and the efforts I put into my company. They also knew that if an extra pair of hands was needed, I was your man. It was that old ethic of always helping out whenever I could. I knew, of course, that I would only ever doze off in comfortable surroundings. I was absolutely secure in the belief that I would never, ever doze off in dangerous circumstances, like driving a car.

Oh GOD!! I'm going to burn.

My feet are hot.

What's all that smoke billowing up out of the dashboard?

Then a face appeared at the car window.

"Tell my daughters I love –"

I was brutally interrupted,

"SHUT UP. That's NOT smoke. It's the gasses escaping from the airbag as it deflates out of the way. You're NOT on fire. Everything will be fine and the ambulance is on its way. Sit tight."

My feelings of terror started to recede, but I was a gibbering wreck, begging to be released from the crushed metal.

"We can't get you out, so the fire brigade is coming to extract you."

Eventually, as I heard the distant sirens, some semblance of reason gained a foothold and I asked

"What about the other vehicle?"

"It's fine. No one was hurt, they're very strong vans – yours is a mess though."

You should see my underwear I thought, but bit my lip.

Blue lights appeared, quite a few of them in the end. Three types of uniform, all buzzing round at once. I will freely admit that there are times when I enjoy being the centre of attention, but not on this occasion.

The police sorted out the traffic, the ambulance men waited around, while the firemen seemed to quite enjoy cutting up the remains of the car with some amazing power tools. Finally there was a gaping hole, where there used to be a car door. The two burly medics worked their way over my various moving parts, and were incredulous that nothing appeared to be broken. I carefully extracted myself, and slowly stood upright. Feeling extraordinarily good to be alive and out of what I had thought was my death trap, my mood was instantly deflated by the nearest ambulance man saying quite firmly

"You will have to get into the ambulance by yourself, you're too heavy for us to lift!"

What a great way to make friends and influence people. I didn't forget that remark in a hurry.

I *did* manage to get into the ambulance, with much support and by being shoved up the steps and was feeling pretty knocked about as I finally lay down on the trolley and we took off for the hospital. Casualty was not much better, with some initial caustic remarks on my size, but they went about checking me over in a thoroughly pleasant and professional manner. It appeared that I didn't need to be admitted and they sent me home with a large supply of pain killers.

By now I was as stiff as a board and so battered and bruised that I couldn't really tell where the pain was actually coming from. I could stand up and walk after a fashion though, and was acutely aware that I was probably the luckiest guy alive at that moment.

Arrival home was accompanied by an excess of feminine fussing (quite pleasant under different circumstances I've no doubt) and brewing of coffee. I finally persuaded them that all I needed at this time in the small hours of the morning was a lie down and some rest. I then discovered that our narrow staircase was out of the question in my condition. Seconds later quilts and pillows appeared to make up a temporary resting place on the large leather sofa. At this point, I discovered that it was acutely painful to even try to lie down, and that the only way to get remotely close to comfortable was to sit in an armchair with a quilt draped over me. And so I settled down for the first of very many nights in that armchair, and began the long, slow process of understanding American football, baseball and the myriad of strange and wonderful things that constitute all-night television.

I sat in that armchair, ironically almost unable to doze off, now that I really wanted to and watched the impressive bruises start to appear in an outline of the seatbelt. The lump, that would eventually grow to the size of a tennis ball just above my heart, was making its first tentative growth spurts and a stiffness that would impair my movement for days was setting like concrete across my body. Underneath all that something else had begun to take shape, deep within my subconscious. It would take weeks to be recognised and accepted, but it was there, a subtle invasive force intent on setting up home in my mind.

The *project* had germinated, and was starting to take root.

CHAPTER TWO

THE STORY SO FAR

IT WAS A BEAUTIFUL AUGUST MORNING IN 1991, AND I WAS HEADING TO The Oval for my very first Test Match against the West Indies. Armed with my corporate invitation (courtesy of a new supplier and typical of those heady days in the City), I was heading for the main pavilion in ample time for the champagne breakfast before the start of play. *The Order of the Day* in my pocket detailed the breakfast, lunch (with many courses), high-tea, post-play early supper and waiter service for drinks, whilst watching play on the pavilion terrace. This was going to be such a good day. I approached the entrance with eager anticipation, walked up to the turnstiles, handed over my ticket, had the stub removed and was about to go through.

"Excuse me, my good fellow. This turnstile is clearly designed only for small children. Where do adults gain access?"

"What're you talking 'bout, mate?"

"This turnstile is too small for a normal adult. This is ridiculous. Kindly arrange to let me through."

"Everyone else gets through OK. Get on with it and stop messing about."

"Don't adopt that tone with me. This turnstile is too small. Show me where I can gain access to the ground."

"Come on, get out of there. Here's your ticket back. Go down the end there to the gate."

In high dudgeon now, I grab the ticket and storm down towards the indicated gate at the end of the row of turnstiles. *This is completely intolerable, how do they expect to get away with treating people in this way!* The man on the gate, innocently going about his duties in the time honoured fashion, received the full blast of my anger.

"You there. Come and open this gate."

"Err – wha'd'you want?"

"I require to be given access immediately. Your turnstiles were clearly and thoughtlessly designed for children only, so get this gate open and let me in."

"Where's yer ticket?"

As I went through the ticket presentation process, the opening of the gate and final access to the ground, I gave this poor chap the full run down on how it was so totally inconsiderate of the world at large not to cater for normal, ordinary people like me.

The arrogance that gave rise to this outburst was fuelled by the culture of working in the City. When a lad brought up in a council house in Hampshire finds himself in a position where moving about London between meetings is not accomplished by tube or taxi, but by calling downstairs for one of the Jaguars and chauffeurs at his disposal night and day; where a PR lunch with a journalist can be taken in one of the private dining rooms, preceded with a discussion with the catering manager as to the menu accompanied by a selection from the corporate wine cellar; where test matches, the rugby at Twickenham, the Proms, the opera at Glyndebourne, front row seats for the British Open snooker final suddenly becomes the stuff of everyday life, it is dangerously easy to start to think way above your station. I was long gone from the City by the time the bonus culture took over, but I can look back and readily understand how this heady atmosphere, totally removed from the everyday lives of ordinary hardworking folk, has got so out of hand on such a global scale.

If, by some strange quirk of fortune, that fellow on the gate at The Oval that day should ever come to read this, I would now like to offer my abject apologies. But this is one of the defence mechanisms of the obese. It is far easier to blame the world at large for being ill-equipped to service the larger members of the population, than ever to admit that it might possibly be our own fault.

For the next few years, the situation got worse and I was in denial to the point where I became able to completely ignore my condition, and the potential consequences. Redundancy in the early nineties came as a total shock, the result of a hostile take-over of the company and the replacement of a number of senior personnel by the new owner's own team.

So I found myself just turning 40, with four lovely daughters, a massive mortgage and no job. Not the sort of situation where you can find the time to worry about yourself. Every waking moment was spent worrying about keeping the house and how to feed and clothe the family. The after effects of the stock market crash of 1987 were still being felt in my section of the financial community – mutual funds – and it proved absolutely impossible to find another job anywhere. There simply weren't any. Luckily a number of companies I knew found that they had a need for some of my skills in this field and so I decided to form my own company and got back on the merry-go-round.

Whilst this meant that at least the mortgage and the financial needs of the family were again being catered for, curiously something which they were able to take entirely for granted, it did nothing to reduce the stress on me. In retrospect it multiplied. My working hours crept up and up, fuelled by the ever present fear that if I didn't do everything humanly possible to look after my client companies, then they could easily take their business elsewhere. That fear eventually became almost paranoia that a single missed phone call could easily prompt a client to try to find their answers elsewhere. At the heart of this was a basic insecurity and lack of confidence in my own skills. I could never bridge the gap between this paranoia, and the simple fact that I had twenty of the largest companies in their field, household names across the country, paying very good fees for access to me. Anyone who has been self-employed (in a one-man band), with immensely powerful clients, who are the dominant partners in the business relationship, will understand how I felt being in that situation for the first time.

At this point the personal computer came along, and although I started to use one fairly quickly, I found it was a two-edged sword. It may seem strange now, in a world totally dominated, in every way, by the computer and the internet, to think that in the early nineties I set the company up and commenced operating in the highly advanced world of the personal investment industry, without a computer. When I think back to my first job working at a tiny country branch of Lloyds Bank, we tallied the tills in Pounds, Shillings and Pence each day on adding machines. *Enter* was achieved by cranking down the handle on the side of the machine; *Save* meant keeping the little printed roll of paper that churned out of the top of the machine.

Reflecting now, I have certainly lived through interesting times.

The computer enabled me to become even more self-sufficient. I no longer had to use the bureau facilities in my serviced office building, but was able to type my own documents, do my own invoices and I soon learnt how to use spreadsheets. On the face of it, this was a good thing in every respect, and I kept abreast of the advances as this new phenomenon moved from DOS to the brilliant Windows environment.

But as time went on, I found that this *good thing* was actually a wolf in sheep's clothing, a Trojan Horse bearing a multitude of gifts from Greeks. This new found ability to operate independently from any form of assistance from support agencies gradually sucked me further into the quicksand of total isolation, and reinforced the need to be constantly available without a break. By now I had started to build up a base of clients in Edinburgh too, and this meant almost monthly trips up to that beautiful city, almost the exact opposite, in style and grace, of London. But day trips were impossible, meaning two or three days away from my desk. This led to a huge amount of debate with myself, ending in the decision to move out from the serviced offices I had inhabited since going it alone, and setting up in my own office, with a personal assistant. The finances made sense, as it was considerably cheaper to rent directly, rather than through a serviced office set-up. The place I found was much closer to home, but this also had a big downside as it was suddenly much easier to pop back to the office for a short while after dinner. This became a habit as I constantly tried to provide the best I could for the family.

This had now become the general state of play; the canvass on which my life was being painted. I had sunk into a self-induced state of high stress where the only thing that didn't matter was *me*. Yet if only I had glanced in the mirror I would have seen that the one thing I should have been taking the most care of was actually me. The future of everything I had created depended upon my well-being, but in those circumstances it becomes impossible to see the wood for the trees.

I had always been fond of my food, and my mother had made sure that I could cook from quite an early age. I developed my skills further through a series of weekend and evening jobs, during the latter stages of my school years, as a waiter in a high class restaurant. Years where I quickly picked up the skills needed to flambé steaks at the table, create Crêpes Suzette before the discerning diners' gaze, and fillet and serve a Dover sole with a fork and spoon in one hand while holding the silver dish with the other hand. This transformed itself over the years to becoming the cook at home, and to passing on most of the skills to most of my girls. Unfortunately, my wife had chosen over the years to use her time for other tasks, and had slowly reduced her involvement in this side of domesticity. Now that I had so little time to devote to this side of things, the quality of my eating habits evaporated almost without trace.

Ten years previously, not long after returning to England in the late eighties, I had actually taken a look at myself, and decided to take action and lose some weight. The favourite diet of the day had been the Cambridge Diet, and I had gone for it in full style. I can even remember attending a corporate function in London, and sitting down with a large number of colleagues for a fine lunch. While they tucked in, as usual, I actually sat with them and ate a meal bar instead, such was the initial commitment. Ultimately, (in my opinion) a 'radical diet' of this type is simply not sustainable, and can never be a substitute for basic, healthy eating. Sadly I could no sooner face a lifetime of solely eating meal replacement bars and drinking meal replacement shakes than I could fly to the moon. Eventually you have to stop (and I did) and the effect on the body is dramatic as it reverts to its initial weight with such a strong bounce that it inevitably ends up worse than when you started.

This little episode was soon forgotten, and perhaps left a small negative attitude toward the effects of dieting in my subconscious. Circumstances took over, and it's only really now that I have even recalled the attempt. But it was interesting to come across some research recently that perhaps goes some way to explaining this *bounce* phenomenon:

> Over millions of years of evolution, the human body learnt to adapt to its environment. In order to survive, it had to learn to store energy to cope with lean periods like winter, so it developed a simple system. It learnt that after every period with plenty of food (summer) there came a period with very little food (winter). Over time the body developed special cells so that

when there was plenty of food it would automatically store as much energy as it could in these 'fat cells', because winter must be coming.

Nowadays we find ourselves in a world where (at least in the developed half) food is relatively plentiful. But evolution is such a slow process that the body has not yet caught up and is constantly expecting that a food winter is about to follow. So it is always trying to store as much as possible in the fat cells, but never getting the lean periods to use it up.

When we go on a 'diet', we effectively give the body the chance to use up this stored fat, by making it think it is in the food winter for which that fat has been stored. However, when the fat cells release their stored energy, they do not cease to exist, but simply sit there waiting until they can be filled again. If we come off the diet, and return to a food summer, the body reacts by not only starting to refill these waiting fat cells, but it tries to increase its efficiency for storage by creating a few more fat cells. Therefore the net result, in the end, is to have used the 'diet period' to actually end up with a greater capacity to store fat.

By the late nineties then, I had lost all sense of proper eating, but without having realised it. It was not something that occurred overnight, but it had crept up on me since becoming self-employed. I had started this period pretty heavy anyway, but that is no excuse either. It became more difficult to find clothes to fit, and I became quite adept at finding branches of *High and Mighty* and catalogues which catered for the fuller figure, and learnt to cope with a really poor choice of styles and colours.

I reached the stage where I simply couldn't properly fit into a normal train seat, but put this down to the modern world's inability to cater for normal, decent people who were a little on the large side. I could actually fit into the seats with the armrests up to accommodate me, (but with sympathy for anyone who had to sit in the reduced space next to me), but it was totally impossible to lower the little table to have a coffee or read a book. It was relatively easy to overcome this inconvenience – simply travel first class where there was enough room. Since most of my clients had been paying for first class travel for their top executives for years, they didn't think twice about paying similar expenses for me.

It took embarrassment to a whole new level when I travelled by plane. I remember an occasion where I found it virtually impossible to fasten my seatbelt. The damn thing simply wasn't long enough to meet in the middle, and I started to sweat wondering if they would have an extension and if not whether I would be ignominiously asked to leave the plane. In the end, I managed to heave up my gut far enough to get the belt done up underneath it, just in the nick of time before the stewardess reached me on her seatbelt checking round. The simple response to this problem? Don't fly anywhere. I added airlines to the ever-growing ranks of what I considered to be anti-social institutions.

In fact by now it was becoming natural to avoid anywhere that had seats and tables that were fixed, which included most café's, bars and wine bars with booths which I could no longer slide into or anywhere that only had chairs with arms. The list just grew and grew.

But this was almost insignificant in the final analysis, as a far more pernicious element came on the scene. Luckily this is now becoming well researched, and much more widely recognised as the potential killer that it is – and I speak, of course, of what we now call sleep deprivation or far more technically *sleep apnoea* (it's funny how acquiring a clinical name gives something a whole new air of gravitas).

Self-denial (read *totally fooling myself*) had now become an art-form. I first started to notice this problem when I was in the middle of typing something on the computer in my office. Suddenly fourteen pages of the letter *h* would appear in the blink of an eye. Or perhaps, when putting pen to paper, I might suddenly realise that in a flash of inspiration I had obviously just acquired the ability to write in some ancient Egyptian sign language, even though I couldn't read it yet! Around the same time I am told that my snoring had reached epic proportions, but the layout of the house and the old stone walls meant that at least the girls could still get some sleep. Obviously this was just down to the length of time I was working, and the stress I was under, and it would ease off as soon as things got a little easier – or so I thought. It was clearly nothing to worry about and hurt no-one but me.

It could easily be countered by a good supply of coffee, and this became almost a standing joke as everyone at work or at home, whenever they made a cuppa wouldn't even ask me but just automatically make one for me as well. I dread to think now of the amount of coffee I consumed on a daily basis at this time, but it was certainly more than 15 mugs a day. This meant that I was also consuming around 40 or 50 spoonfuls of white sugar a day! Food by now had to be fast as I preferred not to spend time eating or cooking, even considering breakfast a waste of time as I needed to be at the office early in case a client called.

Then the situation progressed to the point where I found myself tuning out of the conversation during meetings in the office. My ever loyal staff had the good grace to accept that I was sufficiently confident in their abilities to handle things, while I backed off to think more strategically, or mull over the germ of an idea that had occurred to me from the conversation. What they must have thought in reality I shall hopefully never have to know. The one thing this did do was to make me a little more aware of it, and to make sure I really concentrated that bit harder at external meetings. Strategies were adopted wherever possible – some of them relatively simple. I would always sleep on the train when going to client meetings in London or Edinburgh. During meetings I would always pick the most uncomfortable chair, sit near an open window, accept a coffee immediately or wear my tie too tightly to ensure the discomfort kept me awake. All these little tricks put together would get me through most of the time.

The one thing that I did not realise at the time was that this was a serious condition, and that no amount of tactics would get me through unscathed. The sheer weight I was carrying (not that I had the slightest idea what that actually was) had reached the point where it actually stopped me breathing during deep sleep, forcing my body to react to save itself, and therefore waking me up constantly through the night. As a result I was constantly tired, meaning I fell into the deeper sleep more readily, which in turn meant that I stopped breathing ever more quickly. An extremely vicious circle indeed when left unrecognised and untreated.

By far the most tolerant people at this time were the excellent bunch of guys at my local Rotary Club. I had been invited to join them a couple of years earlier and the Monday night dinners were the only time I spent socialising. It became an ill-concealed standing joke that I would, at some stage, fall asleep during dinner. No amount of tactics could overcome this, as my defences would be down in such a relaxed and friendly atmosphere, and I'm also certain that my glass of red wine with dinner did absolutely nothing to aid the situation. They knew full well that I was working extreme hours, and that I could be counted on whenever help was needed on any projects. Strange as it now seems, one of the regular events of the year was organising The Deepings 10k and Fun Run. One of our members, Tony, had experience in this field and took responsibility for setting it up and organising it all. The rest of us turned up on the day and did as we were bidden while masses of athletic beings came along, ran off down the road and returned a bit later in various stages of exhaustion. I recall that my job would usually be something like handing out the reward mugs (emblazoned with the logo of the main sponsor – another of our members) to the runners as they crossed the finish line.

Another favourite event was turning over our garden, which included a nice stretch of the river bank, for the annual summer Sunday afternoon of jazz, provided by another member who ran his own little jazz combo. This was the one event of the year that my wife attended, mainly because she would have had to go out to avoid it, and it was also a favourite of the girls who would invite their friends who then gained free entry as our guests.

So there I was, by now massively overweight, but under no circumstances prepared to admit to it, denying like mad that I was suffering from sleep deprivation, trying to make a living and keep my home and family ticking over more or less single-handedly.

My four super daughters were growing up rapidly, and were starting to fly the nest. Somehow, we can never clearly work out why or when, it became a standing joke in the family, which then ended up as *normal*, for me to call the girls Number One, Number Two, Number Three and Number Four in order of their original arrival. All their friends know that this is the case, and it has somehow never seemed odd. Number One was living in Liverpool having gone to university up there, Number Two was at university on the south coast, Number Three was at the local college and Number Four was working her way through school (she is the thespian in the family, happiest on stage in anything from Shakespeare to Summer Holiday).

In fact, I had just dropped her off at the Tuesday rehearsal on that fateful night, and had almost reached home, after a very tiring day, when something awoke me from my brief nap. I could see strange red dots in front of my eyes.

CHAPTER THREE

A SECOND CHANCE

AS THE WEEKS HAD PASSED BY AFTER THE CRASH, AND MY BRUISES HAD slowly died down, I was still unable to sleep lying down as it remained too painful. I had moved into what had been the girls' playroom when they were younger, and also set up my computer in there so that I could continue to work on some current projects. The long nights in the armchair dragged by, as a lack of physical activity meant I wasn't too sleepy at bedtime. The mind had an infinite ability to wander quite randomly, and luckily for me it appeared to have no need to re-live the short sharp nightmare of the few moments after the impact. A lump the size of a tennis ball had developed just above my heart, and I had a curious bone spur developing on my left hand, but apart from this, some spectacular, but short-lived, bruising and the inability to lie down, there was remarkably little else to show for the experience.

But the events of that October night had clearly nudged those subconscious thoughts from their hiding place and as the weeks went by they came to the surface. I didn't have any blinding revelations, but became aware of them gradually. In the run up to Christmas there was plenty to keep my mind occupied anyway.

Normally, just before Christmas, I would take a trip up to Edinburgh for the Fuengirola Residents Association Christmas Lunch. Now however official this sounds, believe me there is absolutely nothing *official* about it at all. The FRA is just an extremely diverse collection of old mates who have been taking a weeks holiday together in Southern Spain each year for more years than we care to remember. How it all started is probably lost in the mists of time, but it started with one of the boys, Para Handy to his friends, buying an apartment out there before it became *the thing to do*, and the boys' weeks took place there. He had acquired the nickname as he had a boat in a marina near the apartment in Spain, and Para Handy is the fictional Scottish captain of the SS Vital Spark in the Neil Munro stories about a Clyde steamer. As time moved on, three of the boys bought places there, and so the Fuengirola Residents Association was born. Alongside the week in Spain, the annual Christmas lunch was the one other time we all get together, and it is always held in Edinburgh as that is where all the boys, except me, live. I had first met them when Para Handy and I had gone to Spain for a week to play golf very badly together. My company at the time had employed his Advertising Agency, and we had got on like the proverbial house on fire so had decided to get away together for a week. We had realised too late that the other boys had also arranged to be there at the same time, so we just went ahead and spread into the next door apartment which Para Handy's sister had bought. Luckily I had got on with them all really well, and had, over the years, been assumed into the group as the 'one permitted Englishman'! I was going to say *Honorary Englishman*, but to the boys there is absolutely nothing honourable about being English, and even to this day I can still have trouble cutting through the accents on the relatively rare occasions when they may find themselves a little *tired and emotional* very late at night!

This year, it was going to be impossible to make the trip given the way I was still feeling, so I made my apologies. A day or so after the lunch, Para Handy called me to report on the gathering, and let me know how everyone was. He was very impressed that Big Jim had lost a lot of weight by taking some tablets prescribed by his doctor, and was looking exceptionally well on it. Thinking nothing more of it the conversation moved on, but another piece of information had been filed in those dark recesses of the mind reserved for storing information, ready to surface when appropriate.

I called in to see my doctor on two or three occasions between the accident and New Year, mainly to check that there were no further effects, but also to check the lumps were OK. An X-ray gave my hand the all-clear and the *tennis ball* on my chest began to shrink very slowly. Apparently it had been caused by a large clot from a small blood vessel which burst just under the skin from the pressure of the seat belt, and would break down and disappear in time. Although I had not seen him for some years, he obviously thought it best to concentrate on getting the immediate problems sorted out, and so did not broach the subject of my weight at this stage. I have no doubt that he was simply biding his time and waiting to pounce when I was least expecting it.

Christmas came and went, and with it the family ritual of spending time from late afternoon on Christmas Day till the early hours of Boxing Day playing *Monopoly*. But not just any *Monopoly*, *Star Wars Monopoly* with my Special Edition set. This was now reserved exclusively for Christmas, as the girls knew full well that it was a capital offence to even think about touching it at any other time. As the evening progressed, this would be put carefully away, and we would turn to Texas Hold-em Poker to finish off the night. This is a long held tradition, to the extent that if any boyfriend is to be invited for Christmas, they have to endure training nights if they are not already familiar with the game. They soon learn that this is one family tradition not to be messed with.

New Year's Eve is never what it ought to be, for me. While everyone else is happily celebrating, literally, a New Year, I quietly have my birthday, and lament the fact that I cannot go out for dinner, because every eating house in the country has a special banquet or set meal at an outrageous price. So I usually end up going out for lunch, but the simple fact is that you never get a great lunch anywhere that day, as the good chefs are either already busy preparing the special gourmet banquets for the evening, or are off having a quiet lie down before the storm. So on that lunchtime you are virtually guaranteed to get the apprentices experimenting. Anyway, the family evenings of the past years had faded away as the girls grew up and had better things to do on New Year's Eve, so this year it was a quiet reflective evening at the end of a tough year.

I dozed in front of the same ghastly excuse for entertainment that fills the TV schedule this night each year. My defences were down and the thoughts that had been gradually fighting their way up from the dungeons of my subconscious, decided that now was the time to make their bid for freedom.

Excuse me... shouldn't you be thinking about making some New Year Resolutions?

Don't be daft, I've tried that before, and it's the one time you don't think clearly about the consequences. So failure is a guaranteed result.

This year is going to be different

No it isn't!

Yes it is. This year is going to be very different. You nearly didn't have this year.

What on earth are you going on about?

You could have died in that car crash. If it HAD caught fire, you WOULD have died. It should have caught fire. You have no idea why it didn't.

And so the first seed was sown. The first stirring of the thought process, which would finally lead to my doing something positive, had started. The little conversation inside my head went no further that night, but it had started me thinking more openly about it. Over the next few days it took shape and finally I knew clearly what it was, and what it really meant. It might sound just a little trite now, but it was very real, and it took a firm grip and never let go.

I did *not* die in the car crash. I should, perhaps, have died in the car crash. If so, this was, currently, a *second chance*. If I was to be given a *second chance*, then for heaven's sake, *make better use of it*!!

Once fully formed, this rapidly became a very strong feeling. It was hard to grasp at first, but once I realised it was completely futile to conjecture over *why* I had been given a second chance, or indeed to wonder *who had given it to me*, it became imperative to understand exactly what *making better use of it* actually meant, in practical everyday terms. This was not in any sense a *Road to Damascus* moment, or a *Close Encounter of the Fourth Kind*. It was just a straightforward acceptance that, for whatever reason, and from whatever power, it *was* a second chance, and I *should* make better use of it.

So what should I do? Thinking about this logically, (Spock would have been proud of me), the first thing to do was to make sure that it didn't come to a ghastly halt before I had really got it going. Therefore the first step was to lose weight, so that I wouldn't keep falling asleep and so have another crash.

Right then, I must go on a diet, that will make a first class (late) New Year's Resolution.

I'll start today. In fact right now.

Err, excuse me, but if you are going to lose weight, you will need to know you are losing weight. In order to do that, you need to know what you weigh now, and then see if it goes down.

Sounds logical. I'll get upstairs and get on the bathroom scales right now, and find out what I weigh.

There was, however, a little devil hiding in the detail and waiting to scupper all these good intentions, but I managed to struggle upstairs, and stand on the bathroom scales. To say that I gave them a nasty turn is a bit of an understatement. I gave them such a turn that they shot right round, straight up against the buffers of their maximum of 20 stone.

Oh, not so good, I obviously weigh a little more than 20 stone. No wonder I've had problems.

What should I do now? It would be no good going on a diet, and not knowing if it was working. I'll find another way of weighing myself, and then I'll be able to start the diet. Procrastination is a powerful block to getting started, especially when it is in partnership with deeply rooted fears of what might lie beyond the boundaries of my comfort zone. So I could now perfectly rationalise putting it off till tomorrow – no diet today, you can't *start* without a *starting point*.

MY NEXT STEP WAS TO FIND ANOTHER SET OF SCALES SOMEWHERE THAT would give me my proper weight. I tried one of the big chemists in the city centre. This would do nicely thank you, as they go up to 25 stone. So I slotted in my money, boldly stepped on, and felt quite bad really when they did their version of the nasty turn, and flipped right round against the stoppers. *This really is not good. Why can't someone simply have a set of scales which an ordinary guy like me can use to weigh themselves?* But by now that line was beginning to pale, as I realised that if I was actually way over 25 stone, than I had forfeited all right to think of myself as an ordinary guy. This was unsettling, to put it mildly. I felt like I was heading out beyond the borders of my self-perception into completely uncharted territory. Or maybe I should start referring to it as self-deception?

Within a day or so I had finally found an old fashioned set of scales in a small independent chemist shop away from the city centre. You know the type of scales, with the weights that you move along the swinging arms at the back and able to measure up to 30 stone. Now I was really scared, what if I was over the top here too, that would be disastrous. No, not disastrous, more like appalling, or disgraceful – maybe even shameful! Setting that fear aside, I got on and moved the weights around till it all balanced nicely.

On the 7th January 2005, now aged 51,
I weighed 27.56 stones, or 386 pounds, or 175 kilos.

This was, indeed, shameful, but at last I could start to lose weight. Now all I had to do was to decide how I was going to lose weight, and then put it into practice. *Now let's not go mad here* I told myself. A simple and straightforward way to get going was just to cut out all the snacks and nibbles between meals, and cut down a bit on the portions, second helpings, and extra puddings. Just doing that lot should get things going, while I think about a proper plan. Not sure whether I should tell the wife and the girls, they might get a bit funny about it, and if it doesn't work, I don't want them thinking I'm a failure. I'll just do what I said, keep a low profile, and nobody will probably notice for a day or two. I'll just tell them I'm not feeling great, and therefore not that hungry - that'll put them off the scent for a few days at least.

That night, when I settled down in the armchair, the thoughts would not let me rest. The brain was fairly buzzing with the realisation of just how unbelievably overweight I really was and it was now blindingly obvious that I really did have to do something about it very quickly in order to make this second chance work for the best.

What was that about losing weight quickly?

I have to get on and do this quickly, and properly, before something else happens, as a result of this weight.

No, that's not what I meant. Someone else lost weight quickly recently, someone told us about it. THINK!

Bloody subconscious was developing a mind of its own, and a voice of its own. Have to crack down on that or I'll start to go mad.

Now what was it going on about?

Got it! Para Handy told me about Big Jim at the Christmas lunch, he'd lost a lot of weight quickly – something about tablets from his doctor. I must phone Para Handy in the morning.

I made a phone call to Para Handy, and then the doctor to get an appointment. A day or so later I walked into Dr Ken's room, sat down and took a deep breath –

"Hi Doc, I've decided I need to lose a lot of weight. A friend of mine in Scotland has been prescribed something called *Xenical* by his doctor, and he's lost a fair bit of weight. Is this something I could have to help me?"

From that precise moment onwards, he was terrific. He never pushed me, never judged me, but just quietly supported me all the way. He began by telling me that he was really glad I had taken the decision, because if I hadn't he would have had to start trying to persuade me to lose weight. He thought I would stand a better chance if it had been my own decision, and if I had now properly decided, then he would indeed prescribe the Xenical for me. First, though, he warned me about the side effects, which Big Jim and Para Handy had kept quiet about! The tablets would work, in simple terms, by blocking my gut from absorbing a lot of the fat in my food, and that this might cause a sort of diarrhoea from time to time. If I suffered any other adverse reactions, I was to stop taking them and go back to see him. In the meantime, I was to come back and see him in one month to check on how things were going, and make sure I was still OK not only with the tablets, but with the after effects of the accident. Armed with my prescription I popped into the chemist next door. In no time at all I was heading home to take the first of many of the *blue pills*.

It was also now the right time to tell the family, and seek at least some semblance of support. I did detect, I thought, a rather healthy scepticism, but at least there was an underlying promise of all the support I wanted, if I actually stuck to it myself. I told them about the pills, and as far as they were concerned, if Dr Ken prescribed them, then they must be OK.

To begin with, the pills worked their way up to full effectiveness gently. The first day or so, it was mildly inconvenient to have to make haste to the toilet now and again, but not unworkable, not something to worry unduly about, and certainly not enough to put me off taking the tablets. However, once they built themselves up to full strength, they were capable of testing the patience of a saint.

At this time, I was now working full time from home, and I'm really not sure how I might have coped if I had been taking these tablets and trying to work normally in an office. I'm assured that not everyone has exactly the same reaction to them, but it seems that, perhaps because of my extreme obesity, I was naturally selected for the full side effects. I'm not going to beat about the bush here, but explain things as they were, (but try to keep it gentle by going for the 'black and white' version, rather than the high-definition, wide screen, full glorious technicolor intimate details...).

Let's just back track a little, to the bit about blocking my gut from absorbing a lot of the fat in my food. To cut a long story short, and believe me, at that time, many things got *cut short*. If the fat wasn't absorbed in my gut, then it had to go somewhere, but being fat, it didn't stick to the normal rules, and made its slippery exit just exactly when it felt like it. Also, being essentially, by its very nature, fat (i.e. greasy and slippery), it was problematic to try to stop it from making its exit at whatever pace it chose on each occasion. I made a mental note to ask the doctor when I next saw him whether he could add extra underwear supplies to the prescription, but luckily it escaped my mind again before I could get into trouble repeating it. At this stage, it would have been the simplest, and probably the most understandable, reaction to stop taking the tablets and seek alternative solutions. But I managed to survive for a couple of weeks and then weigh myself again, and was so impressed with my success that I decided to stick with it a while longer. I had managed to stay with my decision to cut out all snacks between meals and during the evening, reduce the size of my meal portions, and stop having seconds, so I was still uncertain as to what to put the weight reduction down to – eating habits or tablets. I just knew that I would continue with both for now, but keep an eye on progress.

When I went back to see Dr Ken in early February, I was down to 25.7 stone, a loss of nearly 2 stone in the first few weeks. Now I know that this sounds spectacular, but when you look closely at it, it really wasn't that wonderful. Given the astronomic weight levels that I started this with, even losing a small percentage represents quite a large actual weight. However, it is only really similar to losing a few pounds from a 12 stone body, and I had the distinct benefit of the extra boost you get when the tablets first go to work. Nonetheless, it was still a great result, psychologically and more than enough to keep me on track, keep me taking the tablets, (and keep me buying the washing powder).

At that second session, he checked my weight, blood pressure and pulse rate, and being satisfied with the findings he duly prescribed another month's supply without hesitation. At this point I asked him for how long he could continue prescribing the tablets, and the answer was basically that he could do so for a very long time, as long as he was sure they were still working for me. This seemed fine, so off I went with another batch of the magic blue pills and an appointment to see him again next month.

These first few weeks were really just a trial period for me, finding out for myself if I could sustain a longer term without the *extras* which for so long had been part of my everyday existence. It wasn't easy, especially being surrounded by the family who were not on a diet, and for whom it would have been totally unfair of me to ban any of these extras just because I didn't want to have them. To be honest, they did not flaunt anything in front of me deliberately, but respected what I was doing and tried to play reasonably fairly with me. The early weight loss was sustained into the second month, and by the time I saw my doctor in March I had lost almost 2 more stone, and was now down to just below 24 stone. He was again delighted with progress. The checks were performed and gave the right outcomes, and another month's supply of Xenical was duly prescribed. But by now I was starting to become a little unsettled by this straightforward approach, and questions were starting to form in my mind.

I recalled the brush years ago with the *Cambridge Diet*, and how the thought of continuing with that regime was impossible. Worst of all, I recalled the resulting *bounce* effect on my weight after coming off that plan. I began to reason that if I was to achieve a long term weight loss, that was sustainable *without* bouncing back up to a high weight again, then it had to be achieved by adopting a plan which I could live with permanently. This also meant that I would have to stop taking the tablets, because I clearly couldn't expect to take them for the rest of my life, nor would I have wanted to. The only problem was that they were working so wonderfully well that I really didn't want to stop taking them at the moment. So I was in a quandary, and needed to find a logical escape route.

Problem solving has always been something I was good at. I've no idea why, but anytime a problem arose, I was usually the one to be asked to find the solution. So I set to thinking this one through. How could I sustain the effect of the tablets in the long run, without pumping the chemicals they relied on into my body? Once I found the answer, it was obvious! The tablets created a block in my gut which prevented the majority of the fat in my diet from being absorbed. By stopping the absorption of the fat, I was losing weight fast. Since my doctor had prescribed them, he was saying that the NHS approved the blocking of fat absorption as a suitable way to combat obesity. Therefore the best way to lose weight, and sustain that weight loss, was to block fat absorption in the gut. But that meant I had just come full circle again, because I didn't want to have to keep taking tablets for the rest of my natural life. So actually I hadn't found the answer at all! This thought process was getting me nowhere, and was starting to tie me in knots.

At this point, it somehow became appropriate to take slightly more interest in what was actually not being absorbed, which was relatively easy to do, as I was producing a fairly regular supply, mostly at quite short notice. The most noticeable fact about *what was not being absorbed*, is that it was actually pretty disgusting, if not totally gross. Without overdoing the detail, it was an orangey shade of yellow, and had a consistency not unlike the tapioca pudding of the 1960's school meals variety. This immediately led to the awful truth that without the tablets, this disgusting stuff would be accumulating inside me and actually becoming what I was made of. This was a truly horrible thought, which immediately mutated into:

There is NO WAY I want that stuff inside me, keep taking the tablets!

But I'd been there, and I didn't want to keep taking the tablets.

OK, if you don't want that stuff inside you, and you don't want to use chemicals to block it, the answer is obvious – don't eat it in the first place, then you won't have to block it!

Oh sweet simplicity! Simply, stunningly, obvious! In fact so blindingly obvious, why on earth had it taken me so long to work it out?

By now April and May's appointments had passed, and I was almost down to 21 stone, a loss of over 6 stone in around 5 months, and I could really start to feel the benefit beginning to have a positive effect in many ways. It had become easier to walk around the place, I was certainly sleeping more peacefully, and in some indefinable way I just felt as if it was *doing me good*, and I mean physically felt it, not mentally. So now I commenced my own little campaign to work out what parts of my diet were responsible for supplying this fat in the first place, so that I could determine what I needed to stop eating. The simple idea in the back of my mind was to change a small part of my daily food intake, and see if that change had a positive or negative effect on the unabsorbed output. In my untutored way, it seemed to me that 24 hours would be enough of a time lag to be able to notice a difference, and that proved to be true for big changes, but it would take longer for the smaller, more subtle changes to take effect.

To be fair, up till now, I had not really made any changes to what was my core diet, as I had been achieving the desired effect just by cutting down the overall level of input, and removing the snacks. Actually, that was not entirely true! I was still having the odd snack, especially during the evenings, but had switched them from the *who cares, just go for it* varieties like chocolate biscuits, crisps, bite-size *Mars Bars*, *Twix*, *Milky Way* and the like, to the so-called *healthy option* type snacks like rice cakes, and anything that claimed to be like crisps but healthier. Complacency ruled now, as I was getting my weight down dramatically with very little effort, thanks to the pills, prompting me to fall into the trap of thinking that this was actually a very easy ride. If I could lose 6 stone in six months, then within a year I would be down to a perfectly respectable weight, and I would hardly have broken sweat getting there.

I began to wonder why on earth everyone thought this dieting thing was so difficult, but then realised that these pills were actually quite a new thing for the NHS to be offering at this time. They would change the world as we knew it and the *magic blue pill* revolution would sweep away obesity in a tidal wave of health across the Western world. I really was feeling positive and relaxed about things when I pitched up to the doctor's surgery for my June appointment, anticipating breaking through the psychologically important barrier of the 20 stone mark for the first time, and probably getting a pat on the back too. I almost bounced in to see him, and strode confidently across to the scales, to register 21 and a half stone.

DISASTER! I HAD PUT ON NEARLY HALF A STONE!

Shattered, I barely realised he was doing the usual round of checks. He started to talk to me, and I pulled myself together a bit, as it was clearly going to be important. I needed to get a handle on this and to I needed to hear him give me an excuse for this unbelievable situation. He didn't give me any excuses, but explained that up till now had been the easy bit, the time where very little effort would achieve maximum results, for a short while. From this point on the going would start to get distinctly difficult, and it was only now that we would actually find out whether I really was tough enough to get on with it and achieve any degree of success at all.

Back home, I slunk off into my corner, and licked my mental wounds feeling quite depressed for a while. This was really not how it had been supposed to progress today. In my twisted frame of mind I came to the conclusion that I had effectively put on a stone and a half that day (as I had expected a loss of at least a stone), therefore the pills were no longer working for me. Luckily, I had to make a dash for the toilet at just that moment, with a stark reminder that the pills were still working perfectly well! So what wasn't working? What had changed? What on earth was I to do about it? This was some sort of crunch point, a turning point along the way, time for some clear thinking, a new strategy, and a need for a proper commitment to it. The realisation I had reached was probably the flashpoint which finally ignited my blue touch paper and got this project off the launch pad.

The only thing that had changed from the time of the accident up to now, was that the blue pills had successfully skimmed off the top of the problem, exposing the true size of the REAL issue. If I had thought I had been successful for the first six months of the weight-loss plan, then I had been utterly deluding myself, as I had not made much personal effort at all towards it. If I had thought that simply by popping pills I could make a better go at life second time around, then this was the wake up call telling me that second chances required effort and commitment. It was high time to stop debating it with myself, analysing why and how it had been like this. It was now time to put in some effort and commitment, and start to actually do what I had been kidding myself I had been doing for the last six months.

It was time to make an effort and lose some serious weight.

CHAPTER FOUR

THE INCREDIBLE SHRINKING MAN

BY 21ST JUNE 2005 I WEIGHED 21½ STONE.

Yes, my weight had fallen by 6 stone in five months, and yes, I should be delighted. But basically it felt like cheating, and there was no way I was going to give myself any credit for it. It would be fair to say that I had cut back on some of my intake, and reduced portion sizes and things, but I had not really put myself under any stress, and relied totally on the tablets. I still snacked from time to time and ate roughly the same things as I had always eaten at home. Even though I had not visited a fast food outlet for a while, it was more because I wasn't encountering any in the current routine, than because I had the determination to drive past them.

Putting on half a stone in the last month had made me realise, with a vengeance that this was not going to happen if I continued in this way. I needed to get back to where I was at the start, not physically, but mentally. And this shock had knocked me right out of the comfort zone I had sunk into, and reminded me what this was supposed to be about. This was my second chance, and I had to grasp it now, before it escaped. I would certainly never get a third chance!

Stop dithering. Stop getting all emotional. Cut to the chase and get a plan!

Right then, Plan B coming up.

Although, on reflection, Plan A was good, I just forgot about it and slid off sideways.

Where was I again?

This took me a few days, but eventually I found my focus and got back to the job in hand. I simply had to find a way to lose weight, but by doing so in such a way that I could sustain it permanently, and that meant getting off these tablets as soon as possible. So I came back to the idea that rather than take these tablets in the way that they were intended, which was basically as a substitute for hard work and dedication, I would experiment with them to see what I should or shouldn't eat. At the same time, I would finally get serious about cutting out everything that remotely resembled snacks, or treats, or extras in any way.

In some ways, I can now see that the June weigh-in was almost a mini-repeat of the car crash, psychologically. It knocked me right back to the idea of grasping this second chance, and really making more of myself than I had the first time round. I had no idea what that might end up being, but I certainly knew what had to be done in order to make the chance real, and open up the options. I had to get right back to square one and get myself down to the sort of weight I was before the family came along. I had to set myself a proper target, get down to around 15 stone, and fast. I wasn't getting any younger, after all.

The object became clear again on the food front. I had to keep taking the tablets, but I had to change what I was eating until the horrible by-product ceased to be produced. My logic remained simple, but was now even clearer. If I could reach a stage where my usual food intake was pleasant, sustainable and not weird in any way, but the tablets no longer produced any side effect, then this would mean I could stop taking the tablets without a detrimental effect. This would also mean that my regular diet would be more or less correct because, my twisted logic ran, it would be NHS-approved by definition. It had to be, because they approved these tablets to stop me absorbing what was wrong, so if they had nothing to stop being absorbed, then I couldn't be eating anything wrong. Now I no longer saw the tablets as fat absorption blockers, but as a food approval system, and a temporary one at that.

I started to take a closer interest in the *output*, making small sustainable changes and watching for the results. I didn't automatically write-off things because they were widely regarded as being wrong, or unhealthy, or fattening. I chose to completely ignore any conventional sources of *wisdom* on the subject, mainly because many of these seemed inevitably linked to the requirement to pay money to those who created them. Rather, I chose to use my *blue pills* as the sole arbiter of right and wrong in the 'shall this pass my lips' stakes, and before long I was able to see obvious ground rules emerging.

The most obvious thing of all was fat. Now there's a surprise! If the primary purpose of the tablets was to block fat absorption, then I needed to eat less, or virtually no, fat. The secret was in spotting where fat was present in food, and although most fat is pretty obvious, it is a devious component of some seemingly innocent foods. I had long since become responsible for the main weekly shopping, and I now found myself becoming a student of food labelling, and this was long before the introduction of the new *traffic light* symbols on packaged food in supermarkets, and fancy DEFRA inspired alternative labelling systems. I rapidly got used to doing without butter or margarine, or some of the other vegetable oil based spreads, on any sandwiches or toast, and much as I regretted it, cheese was reduced to a very rare treat. Strangely though, and this has applied over time to any number of things, reducing it to the status of rare treat has significantly enhanced the enjoyment when the appropriate occasion does arise.

Now it was time to face my nemesis Dr Ken at my July visit. This time rather than the assured bound onto the scales of the fateful June visit, it was more a cautious, timid creep onto them. But the bounce in my step was back as a weight of 20 stone exactly was announced. I made my first (and last) attempt at a *Dettori Dismount* from the scales which did not end as gracefully as I might have wished! This show was clearly back on the road. The blood pressure and heart rate were both as good as they had been, and nothing untoward was indicated, so a further prescription was written out. At this point I decided to explain to my doctor what I was doing, that is, using the tablets to indicate good and bad changes to the diet. He saw no problems, and thought it was an interesting approach, and endorsed it as long as I kept on losing weight and maintaining good pulse and blood pressure.

Slowly, very slowly, I was making the first tentative steps towards a healthier eating style, but as it often does, life was planning other little traps in the hope of catching me unawares. The whole second chance assessment plan was growing stronger as it fed on the success in the weight area, and I began to think about other changes to complement the progress. For many years now we had lived in a large house with a very large garden, on the bank of a small river. I had managed to bring the garden under control over the years, from the starting point of a total wilderness, with the help of a wonderful retired stonemason from the East End of London who had moved up nearby years ago. Recently he had found himself a new, special lady and had left me to fend for myself as he moved away to live with her. Unable to find a replacement I was rapidly reaching the point where I no longer saw any beauty in the garden, just a list of jobs a mile long in every direction. The house itself, which had barely been big enough when bringing up the four girls, was now becoming a shell of empty and unused rooms with three of them having moved out, and had been quite beyond any motivation that my wife had, to maintain it in anything remotely resembling good order.

So the next decision was to sell the house, and move to something much smaller and very much easier to maintain. In the light of what has subsequently happened to the housing market, this was a very lucky piece of timing, as I would certainly not have wanted to try to sell it later. However, having both agreed that this was the best course of action, and approached some local agents to value and market it, neither of us was really prepared for an offer at virtually the asking price within a day of placing it for sale. In fact we had received the first offer before the sign was erected, closely followed by a second offer, but with strings attached. This more or less coincided with my August visit to Dr Ken, and the happy news that my weight was now down another 9 pounds, with no bad signs anywhere, so again it was *'keep taking the tablets'* (but only on my terms).

As we drifted into September, with the lawyers beavering away on the paperwork, and me beavering away sorting out the house, and trying to make more sense of my diet, professionally it was proving an interesting time as well. I had started working with a new contact introduced to me by a mutual friend, and we were getting on extremely well as we had very different, but entirely complementary skills. One of the effects of this collaboration was the decision to launch a new company trading exclusively on the internet, and at the launch at the beginning of September we almost immediately received an offer for the company from a large group with aspirations in the same area. The decision to accept the offer was simple, and I was subsequently embroiled in the immense amount of paperwork that these deals generate, especially when the other party is employing a top London corporate law firm. For the next few weeks I was under an enormous amount of pressure dealing with lawyers in every direction, trying to get the house sorted out ready for a move, and still trying to cope with the weight loss programme. At first everything went smoothly, no major hiccups anywhere, and I was even more encouraged when September's check showed another 9 pounds off, down to 18¾ stone (262 pounds or 119 kilos). I had now lost cumulatively almost 9 stone, or 56 kilos.

As October arrived we reached an agreement to complete on the house sale at the end of January, so as not to disrupt the Christmas holidays. The purchasers were a local couple who had recently sold their business and they were in absolutely no rush to complete as they were not going to move in straight away but make some serious alterations to the place. Unfortunately, once everything had been signed up, I was confronted with the fact that I was virtually going to have to deal single handedly with sorting out the house, downsizing its contents, and making all necessary arrangements, as all practical domestic support had been effectively withdrawn. This also now applied to my efforts to lose weight, something which I had been trying to encourage my wife to join in as her own health could certainly have benefited significantly from a similar loss. However, for her own reasons, she took the view that it was not the right time for her to do that, and also decided that she was not going to be a party to disposing of the mountains of weird and wonderful stuff she had collected and hoarded in the spare rooms in case they were ever needed, or for when the girls started making their own homes.

I am not including details here in order to judge or be judged, but simply to explain how such extreme stress led to the derailment of the project. For derail it certainly did.

October's weigh in showed a gain of ½ a stone, accompanied by a relaxed piece of advice from my doctor that I should not expect a constant drop, and the odd occasion where it fluctuated was only to be expected.

The following three months were a slow spiral downwards into an emotional quagmire which I am most definitely going to skirt over with an alacrity born of sensitivity for the various participants. I distributed enough clothing from the various hiding places around the house to a variety of charity shops in the area to keep their shelves and racks filled for months. The local auction rooms gave what assistance they could, and I lost count of the number of skips that departed loaded to the gunwales. Along the way, over 30 years of marriage sank into a decision to have a period of separation, accompanied by the decision to rent a small house for her and the cat and dog, and a small flat for me and Number 4, who took no time at all to decide who she wanted to live with. The other three took the decision in their stride and expressed the view that in their opinion it had been too long in the making and they were relieved that it had finally been taken. Sad really, that they had seen it coming long before we did.

The only respite in this difficult period was my insistence on making the annual trip to Edinburgh for the FRA annual Christmas lunch. I set off with some trepidation, especially as I was facing the prospect of a night in a hotel when I was still not able to sleep in a bed. I was hoping that there would be a substantial armchair in my room so that I could at least try to spend the night in some sort of comfort. Although I was acutely aware that I had not seen any of the boys since long before the accident, it never occurred to me once to realise that they had not seen me in weight loss mode. As usual, as I had travelled the furthest (at least on the day), I was the first in Mather's for the pre-lunch drinks. It was then that I finally realised that I had a new and different appearance, as the boys arrived one at a time and at first weren't certain that they recognised me till I spoke to them. When Para Handy finally turned up, there was quite a gathering already, and in his inimitable style he encapsulated the moment by declaring:

"Oh my God, it's **The Incredible Shrinking Man!**"

By now being pressed from all sides to explain, I told them about the accident, how Para Handy had passed on the information about Big Jim's tablets, and how the rest was becoming history now. The saddest part about that day was seeing that Big Jim was still Big Jim. He had not been prepared to cope with the side effects, had stopped taking the tablets and rapidly reverted to his original size and shape. As usual, the rest of that day quickly passed into a haze of typically epic proportions, but it was rapidly becoming clear that my group nickname had already changed by popular acceptance to The Incredible Shrinking Man, and this was born out in all the email chatter from that day onwards. I will not deny that I was perfectly happy at this turn of events, not so much from the nature of the new nickname, whose eventual ramifications were still unknown, but from finally and legitimately losing my old nickname which derived from my surname *Hare*. Yes, I had always been *The Pubic*. After a relatively quiet, but short, alcohol-sedated night in the armchair in my hotel, I returned home suitably refreshed.

A truce was declared for the last Christmas in the family home, and the year eventually drew to a close. January saw the final clearing out of the house, which suddenly, with all of the clutter gone, seemed enormous again. The agreements were signed for the two rental properties and the lawyers actually managed to complete on the sale of the house without a single solitary dot out of place. The new owners came round a few times, and while the ladies discussed what ladies discuss in the house, I gave the necessary lessons in driving and using a ride-on lawn mower, and how to use the various raking, slitting, spiking and rolling implements that dramatically impaired its ability to mutate into a poor man's five speed quad bike. I managed to repatriate all the sets of keys that the girls had been trying to avoid handing back until the last possible moment, and we were finally ready to move out.

We had rented the new places with a few days overlap, so that by the time the final handing over of the keys ceremony came to pass there was nothing to do but literally walk away. I had already made certain that everything was properly set up in both places, and everything was in full working order. We had both actually moved out a day or so before completion, so on the appointed day it was purely a question of turning up, have the lawyers confirm everything was in order, hand over the keys, shake hands and walk away. So that's exactly what we did.

I had begun by thinking it would be a wrench to leave ***the house*** *after 18 years, but when it came to the crunch, I just walked slowly and quietly away. A line had been drawn in the proverbial sand.*

I had begun by believing that it would be a wrench to leave ***the marriage*** *after 30 years, but when it came to the crunch, I just walked slowly and quietly away. Another line had been drawn in that same proverbial sand.*

There was nothing but the future now, not that I really had a single clue as to what it might be, but that was what made life fun.

Oh my God – when was the last time I actually thought that life was fun? All right, then – lets see if it turns out that way!

And so it was that one of life's chapters drew, quite literally, to a close.

CHAPTER FIVE

GOING IT ALONE

MY WEIGHT HAD REMAINED CONSTANT AT AROUND 19¼ STONE FROM October through to the January of 2006. Nothing more came off, but at least nothing went back on again which is quite amazing given the circumstances, as my weight had hardly been high on the agenda throughout that difficult time. But now I found myself in a completely new environment, playing to a new set of rules which, to be honest, I hadn't even written yet. Change is too simple a word to describe the next few weeks. It was like being parachuted into a new world without a guide book.

Bizarrely, the first significant change I made was to buy a bed. Nothing fancy, just a plain simple, yet sturdy pine frame with a very firm mattress, and some new bedding to go with it. It was delivered flat packed, but was extremely easy to knock together. The key to the significance of this purchase lay in the fact that I had not slept in a bed since the accident, 15 months previously. It was somehow a symbolic purchase, and I was delighted when I actually slept comfortably and peacefully the first night in it. It was almost as though I could finally rest easy again after a very traumatic series of events, and this seemed to set my mood for the next few months.

I was now in total control of shopping, cooking and eating, and the interest I started to take in food labels again could see me taking hours on a simple shopping trip. This control meant that I could completely dedicate myself to the task of adjusting the diet until the tablets were rendered obsolete. So I started to take more notice of the ingredients of all my purchases, and every now and again found a little spare time to scour the internet for what I hoped were sources of unbiased but technically correct information on nutrition. There are about as many sources of *advice* out there as there are people prepared to pay for them, so I studiously and carefully avoided anything which called itself advice or help, but required the purchase of branded goods or special supplements.

The early experiments with a very low fat diet were doubly successful. The most immediate effect was that I could start to spend longer periods of time further than two minutes from the nearest toilet without the requirement to carry spare underwear. More satisfying, though, was that by the February visit to Dr Ken I had lost about ¾ of a stone and was down to 18½ stone, and by March I was right down to just over 17¾ stone. This was almost 10 stone in 14 months, and I was *ecstatic*.

However, I had begun to really struggle now with one major problem I simply hadn't thought about at. I had virtually nothing to wear. Now I am well aware, ladies, that this is usually taken to *mean nothing suitable for the occasion*, but in my case now it was entirely literal. I had long since passed on the clothes I was wearing at my *peak*, either to charity shops or to scout troops to use as small mess tents for camping trips. Now I was finding that the clothes that I had previously grown out of (but kept in hope), and had then grown back down into, were now too big in every respect too. The problem was how to replace them. I don't mean that it was a problem to find clothes to fit, as I had gained years of experience finding jumbo sized clothes. The problem was that I was extremely confident that I would lose more weight yet, so virtually anything I bought now would have a very limited lifespan before moving on to the Salvation Army or Age Concern. The real problem was therefore, how few clothes I could get away with, to save having to spend a fortune every few months on a complete new wardrobe.

That spring and summer were spent avoiding anything remotely like a 'Formal Dress Do', and keeping a relatively low profile in jogging pants and sweat shirts. Track suit bottoms and the like had an extended lifespan for me solely down to the drawstring waist and acceptable floppiness. And remember, I also had the distinct security of knowing that absolutely nobody I knew expected me to look sartorially elegant in any way, shape or form! Another advantage I had going for me was that I had reduced social contact across the board mainly from the move to a different part of the locality, although partly because my strong desire to avoid any sort of food or meals that didn't match my new low fat regime meant that I resigned from the Rotary Club.

The other characteristic of that period was the highly desirable side effect of the weight loss meaning that I had a good deal more energy than I was used to. The result was the easy decision to spend a little spare time every day going for a walk along the riverside path that passed in front of the flats. I had never seen this area before, and was fascinated to find a whole world of sports fields, meadows and nature reserves virtually on my doorstep, and leading out from the very heart of the city. From the early lunchtime strolls of a few hundred yards, these rapidly became voyages of exploration into unknown territories, and unwittingly they took on the guise of what I later calculated were 3 to 4 mile walks on weekend afternoons. I found myself making regular checks on the progress of the nesting swans, looking out for the herons and caught fleeting glimpses of kingfishers as I got to know their individual hunting grounds. The psychological benefits of this inadvertent private time for me, and the physiological benefits of the exercise I was getting from these outings, produced a powerful cocktail of positivity that I had not really experienced before. I actually began to make significant strides towards feeling good about myself, and it was only when I realised what was happening that it even began to dawn on me that maybe that had not been the case lately.

By now I had become confident enough in the changing nature of both my eating habits and my toilet habits to start making rules. Now by this I mean that the few changes that I had made to my usual food intake had reached the point that I was now confident that they were achieving a positive contribution in their own right. (The toilet related output had seen significant improvement!) The changes became my rules. They may not sound like earth shattering revelations, and in most cases they are now accepted wisdom. But my innate cynicism about the world of dieting and weight loss had led me to believe that all advice, on any aspect of eating, had an equally powerful and diametrically opposed lobby, and that both sides had an *agenda* behind them. It had been fundamental to me to test them out myself before becoming completely comfortable with them.

So my first set of Ten Commandments became:

- **Semi-skimmed milk only**
- **No white bread, only wholemeal, preferably with wholegrain as well**
- **No potatoes. Substitute wholegrain rice, and wholemeal pasta**
- **No cheese**
- **No butter or margarine**
- **No puddings, only fresh fruit**
- **Absolutely no snacks of any kind**
- **Eat three proper meals a day**
- **Go for a walk every day**
- **Do NOT weigh yourself more frequently than once a week**

April's visit to the doctor was a delight, as I weighed in at 17¼ stone, down just over half a stone again that month. This meant that I had now officially, and clearly by some margin, broken through the 10 stone barrier at last. He continued to express amazement at my steady and determined progress, and confirmed that once again there was nothing wrong showing up anywhere physically. My blood pressure was fine, I still had a pulse, and he would see me next month as usual. By now I think I had seen him more times in the last 15 months than I had actually seen him in the previous 15 years, and although it might seem strange to be visiting him to confirm that there was nothing wrong with me, these visits were still essential to my peace of mind. I needed someone of his experience to tell me that I was doing well, because most of the time everyone else saying it came into the category of *they would say that anyway*. I also needed to know that I was not inadvertently creating any other problems that were going to crawl out of the woodwork and bite me when I was least expecting it.

As April passed into May that year, the evenings (and my heart) lightened, and I extended my nature walks to the extreme limit of the time I could spare for them. By now I was able to pass by a burger stand and experience the aroma without feeling the need to buy one. I could sit in the same room as someone eating chocolates and not want one myself. My diet felt good, I was full of energy, and I began to wonder about what I could add to the mix to keep up the momentum. That was when my mind strayed off down a new secret passageway I had no idea existed. I have no clue about what prompted it initially, as nothing in my entire experience had ever strayed in that direction before. The thought, that occurred totally out of the blue and then took up residence with full nagging rights, was... shock horror...

Join a gym.

What did you just say?

Join a gym.

Don't be daft, why would I join a gym?

To get better exercise than walking, to get fitter, and it will help with the weight loss.

Don't be so downright stupid! I would stand out like a sore thumb in a gym and have all those fit young types sneering at me. FORGET IT!

About this time, (the sub-conscious me was getting too clever for its own good), I began to realise that there was, in fact, a side-effect to this weight loss that I simply had not considered, in the slightest. It was something that had obviously lain dormant waiting for the appropriate moment, and it now decided to show its head. Skin! Now skin is one of the most amazing parts of the human anatomy, it has almost endless elasticity, probably best demonstrated by my own experience. But it does have one or two small shortcomings, if the truth be recognised, and it was now being recognised full on. When you lose 10 stone it is from the layers of fat that build up under the skin, and which the skin has assiduously grown, quietly and efficiently, to keep covered. However, when you rapidly remove vast quantities of the fat beneath the skin, it does not suddenly and miraculously turn into shrink-wrap, but begins to take on the qualities of a duvet kicked back on first getting up in the morning. It hangs around in strange, wrinkled, bunched-up lumps, or droops over the side of the bed in a desperate attempt to reach the safety of the 'fall-no-further' floor. The full truth of this phenomenon hides behind the joint distractions of the satisfaction of having lost the weight in the first place, and the beguiling lightness of what is left compared to its illustrious God-like (I'm thinking Buddha here) predecessor. It was not a serious problem, but it did lend weight to the thought that joining a gym might be a good idea. Anything which could assist in keeping the loose bits under control had to be a good thing.

On the food front, I had begun to try out different cooking methods, in an attempt to find a way of preparing my food, as far removed from microwaving *low-fat* ready cooked meals as possible. The principal downside of most of the methods was the time they took up in a busy day, and the need for careful menu planning. I had by now decided that the wealth of information available on the subject was true. Food was far better being undercooked than overcooked (with notable exceptions like chicken I know) and the classic *al dente* method keeps most of the vitamins intact until they reach the plate. My method of choice, the one that satisfied both the time and texture issues, was stir-frying in my wok. Through trial and error I developed an expertise in the timing of each ingredient of a meal so that it retained taste, texture and nutritional value. A decent rack of herbs and spices opened up a wonderful world of flavour options, and the speed of cooking, in this way, was mind boggling. The main key to my cooking has always been a strong sense of freedom from rules – if I have one main rule in the kitchen it would be: **Be the cook, not the critic**.

Think about it for a minute. What is your absolute all-time favourite recipe? Now cast your mind back to when someone, in a kitchen somewhere, or maybe by an open fire in the countryside, actually put those ingredients together in that way for the very first time ever, and applied heat in some way. Do you want to be that cook, or do you want to be the person who was stood beside them, looking over their shoulder, saying,

"Don't be stupid, that's a waste of good food, it'll taste ghastly".

Now I don't want you to gain the wrong impression here. Cling to the thought that whatever else I may be, I am still just a guy in his fifties, with a healthy (?) regard for good food. You will never catch me stuffing vine leaves with Mongolian tofu, or serving Tiramisu dressed with a light jus of blended pomegranate and guava berries. I'm quite content to leave that to the fawning followers of escapees from a tyre factory – you know, the Dunlop people, or is it Michelin? I occasionally like to watch these people at work, but I think you see them at their most *realistically* skilful in the sorts of programmes where they are given a set of ingredients at the last minute, and have to knock out a meal in a few minutes. That is when I get interested both in the strange combinations of ingredients, and just how quickly you can cook food properly.

So when it came to the time for my May medical check, I was feeling good, getting better organised at life in general, and my dietary habits were coming together in a pleasing way. Yes, the sub-conscious was starting to pursue its own agenda as usual, but it was still too stuck in the subtle phase to have any major effect. The scales didn't let me down and showed 16 stone 9lbs, that's more than another half a stone gone *forever*. Blood pressure was creeping ever further down and my heart rate perfectly fine. Keep on keeping on was the message I got.

On the way back from the surgery I was letting my mind wander euphorically through the clouds when the sub-conscious launched another surprise attack.

Just think how much better, even now, you would feel with some proper exercise, and you could save all that time spent walking,

But I like that time walking.

Well, carry on doing that as well.

Now a few years previously a large fancy gym had been built on the outskirts of the city, which was effectively the only one that I knew existed. Was it fate, was it the mind playing tricks on me, or was it pure coincidence that this mental exchange took place on the dual carriage-way approaching the roundabout with the exit to that very gym? I decided to consign that one to life's filing cabinet under *lesser mysteries*, park the car, and ask for a tour.

Well, to be perfectly honest it was literally the first time I had ever been inside one of these places, and I was completely staggered by the facilities it had to offer. The gym was packed with some of the weirdest looking contraptions that had clearly been designed during an experimental engineering seminar at the annual convention of the world's leading authorities on sadomasochism. But the studios, swimming pool, saunas, steam rooms, spa pools, hair salon, aroma therapy rooms, and not least the café-bar were about as far from my *Rocky* expectations as it was possible to get.

Yes, there were almost enough mirrors around the place to satisfy the needs of the few gym bunnies whose principal purpose in attending always seems to be to acquire sufficient flexibility and muscle definition to be safely told that they are *the fairest of them all*. Every gym has them, and always will have them! Infinitely more pleasing was the realisation that there were, in fact, a majority of people to whom the term *muscle definition* meant the list on the wall chart in the physiotherapist's office.

My fear of sticking out like a sore thumb amongst an elite gathering of the city's finest athletes proved to be utterly groundless, and I was still a little dazed when I left after having signed up for a year's membership.

Had there been a disturbance in *the force*, had some seemingly innocent little butterfly in an Asian rainforest casually flapped its wings? Not only had I joined a gym, but when I got back, I actually got out my diary and, as instructed, made an appointment for my first induction session. Then a small problem struck me. I had no trainers, shorts, vests or in fact anything that was remotely suitable for wearing to a gym. This could *not* be happening – joining a gym *and* going shopping all in one day?

Oh my God! What if I can't find anything to fit me?

I headed for the big chain sports shops in the city centre with huge trepidation, but was chuffed to bits when, for the very first time in donkey's years, I actually went into a high street shop and bought items of clothing off the peg that fitted me. This was turning into one hell of a good day! I bought shorts, some T-shirts, a pair of simple basic trainers and some white socks on special offer that day – five pairs for £3 or something like that. I even had the sudden presence of mind to buy a sporty looking hold-all which looked so much better than the supermarket carrier bag I would have been forced to use, but for this brainwave. Did I need anything else? Frankly, I didn't have a clue.

I did wonder at this point whether I should have consulted my doctor on this *small step for mankind - giant leap for obese kind*, but decided not to worry but remember to tell him about it when I next saw him. So, trusting that I had indeed covered all my bases, I felt fully equipped and ready to go.

Off I went for my very first gym session, with my new bag, full of my new kit, contentedly assured that I would *not* stand out like a bacon sandwich at a Bar Mitzvah.

CHAPTER SIX

INTO THE UNKNOWN

I DULY TURNED UP AT THE GYM AT THE APPOINTED HOUR, AND CHANGED into my new kit, suddenly wishing that I had at least washed it a few times and removed the blatant brand new look they screamed out to everyone within a hundred mile radius. I found my way upstairs to the gym floor, and introduced myself to Dave, who would be my fitness instructor. I was then sat down in a very comfortable armchair, and subjected to the Spanish Inquisition on everything that could possibly be relevant as to why I was there, and a whole lot of stuff that I thought wasn't remotely relevant. I quickly realised that this was all for an excellent purpose, as quite clearly I didn't want to be thrown in at the deep end and induce a heart seizure almost as much as they didn't want to end up being held responsible for it. We agreed, in the end, that my *targets* would be first of all to increase my general fitness level and secondly to lose a stone in weight. They were very much against setting targets too high, firmly believing in the maxim that targets should be small and achievable. This way success early in the game would continue to provide a positive background to making further progress, rather than continually failing to achieve a target that was actually just a little out of reach. I understand this completely, as it should be the basis for all weight loss targets. Don't ever try to set out to lose 4 or 5 stone, as it is such a big thing to aim at. Rather, aim to lose a pound a week, which is thoroughly achievable for virtually anyone. If you actually manage to lose a pound a week, on average, for a year, then that adds up to nearly 4 stone, but with success every week to keep you going.

My initial programme, to be attempted at least three times a week, but preferably five times, was set up for *feeling my way* in to this sort of thing. It involved the use of three core machines designed specifically to work on my cardiovascular fitness, the rowing machine, the treadmill and the reclining bike. CV exercise, as it is known, is the basic relatively simple exercise that targets your heart and lungs. To get fitter, and to move onto any form of more intense exercise, you have to start by making sure that your heart is strong enough to pump blood round your body to carry the extra oxygen to your muscles for their extra work. CV work allows you to push up your heart rate in gentle steps. As the heart is essentially just a complex set of muscles, regular CV exercises will build up those muscles in the same way that you can build up your biceps using weights.

Each session would comprise:

- **5 minutes on the rowing machine at resistance level 5**
- **10 minutes on the treadmill, walking fairly fast, with a 1% incline**
- **10 minutes on the reclining bike at resistance level 4**

Depending upon how I felt, I could gently increase times, resistance levels or both over the next few weeks, but I should talk to Dave from time to time and let him know how I was getting on with it, and what increases I was achieving.

The first couple of times that I went through the programme I was really just getting used to the machines, and soaking up the ambience of the place. I continued to be pleasantly surprised at fitting in quite easily to the type of clientele that frequented the gym, and the friendly banter that generally went on most of the time. None of my fears proved to be grounded in any way, and even now it would be fair to say that I have never felt out of place, or uncomfortable (in the social sense), at any session I have ever done. By my third session I was ready to up the ante, as there was no point in going there and using the equipment if I wasn't pushing myself even a little. Clearly the lengthening walks along the river had given me a base to work from, but if that was the case then I had better 'work from it', rather than just maintain it.

In my first week I did five sessions, and I started my second week with:

- **15 minutes on the treadmill**
- **10 minutes on the bike (resistance up to level 6 now)**

- **7 minutes on the rower**
- **Another 15 minutes on the treadmill**
- **Another 15 minutes on the bike (once again at resistance level 6)**

Already my 25 minute workout sessions had become 62 minutes. As each day went by, I began to feel my spirits lifting; I had a lighter step and my movement was easier, as if an unseen hand was gently easing some hidden weight off my soul.

Essentially I spent that first month at the gym finding a level of good, strenuous exercise that I could maintain over the weeks and that would push me by just the right amount, and progress it as my body kept pace. I also got to know all the fitness team, and quite a few of the other members who seemed to find themselves there at roughly the same time as me most days. The whole experience had turned out to be a lot more sociable than I had ever dreamed possible. Another benefit was that it was getting me out of the flat more frequently, and I was slowly gaining a whole new circle of acquaintances, all of whom knew nothing of my past and simply accepted me for what I was now.

With all this going on I settled for a simple maintenance of my current eating habits, and didn't bother with any more trial and error changes. I could no longer be sure whether any results would be because of dietary change or the new exercise programme. The only way to know for sure was to only change one thing at a time, and as I was definitely changing the exercise side of things, this required dietary stability. So I was eating the same as I had been before, sticking to my three meals a day and nothing in between, and with the exercise programme now swinging into gear with a vengeance I was expecting big things at the monthly check up in June. I knew it would be good, as I was already starting to feel that the exercise was doing me a power of good, and I was definitely detecting a small change in the way my current crop of clothes fitted. I headed for the doctor with hopes of a really good weight loss result this month.

16 stone 1 lb the scales told us. I was just a tiny bit disappointed, to tell the truth. Yes, it was just over half a stone off again, but in the back of my mind I was definitely hoping for more. Blood pressure and heart rate checks followed. Just as I was thinking that I must tell my doctor

about starting to go to the gym, he said out of the blue, as if he was reading my mind:

"Well Mike. When did you start properly exercising then?"

I was dumbfounded, but managed to mutter something about the gym.

"I thought that might be the case. It's a great idea, and will back up what you're doing, tremendously."

How on earth did he know? Had he seen me there and not said? Had a mutual acquaintance told him in passing that I was there?

"How did you know I was exercising?"

He then explained that he had been able to spot it immediately from my blood pressure and heart rate readings, together with the fact that my weight was still reducing really well. The truth is simply that even with just the simple exercise routine that I had been doing, a little fast walking, a bit on the rower and a bit on a bike, the effect on my heart was immediately noticeable. He also pointed out that it should be becoming harder to lose weight now as I was long past the point of shedding the easy stuff and was beginning to get down into my hardcore fat reserves.

I want to stress this point here and now. This was a big lesson for me, but is a clear message to everyone. I know we hear all the time that exercise is good for you, and we all probably *think* that this true. But I guess we all think that *good for you* is just a figure of speech, not a quantifiable reality that has the power to change lives. The plain fact is that a few short weeks of doing some of the most basic exercise was so *good* for me that a doctor could tell straight away by just checking my blood pressure and heart rate. This taught me a lesson in no uncertain way, and please let it be a lesson to you.

At this point I also raised another small problem that had been getting a little on my nerves, especially since starting the gym programme. The skin left on my stomach was beginning to hang down worse than ever, and whilst it was a wholly acceptable by-product of my efforts (and I preferred that to its predecessor), it was starting to cause little rashes and itching to develop beneath *the flap*. This had become more pronounced with the exercise, as it was made worse when I worked up a bit of a sweat. I had mentioned it in passing a month or two previously, but with little conviction, and no response. This time, however, he decided to have a look at how *the droop* was developing and after prodding and much humming, he told me it was now time to refer me *up the food chain* to the reconstructive surgery team and see if we couldn't have it removed. Stunned silence from me. Finally, I asked:

"What? On the NHS?"

"Of course. You have done so brilliantly with this whole weight loss project. You are sticking at it and doing exercise to help it go further, so of course we will help you."

He went on to explain that it would essentially be up to the surgery team, but he would refer me and I could expect to hear about an appointment in a few weeks time. If the surgeon was happy that the operation would be a success, then I would go onto his list and *the droop* would be consigned to memory. I was absolutely flabbergasted that this was possible. The thought had crossed my mind vaguely in the past, usually prompted by some extreme TV show stumbled across by accident, but I could not accept that what I was achieving was in any way special or out of the ordinary, I was just a guy who had got way too big, and was putting it right. The thought in the back of my head had always been that surgery of that nature was something that people paid to have done privately, and at enormous cost (and well beyond my humble means and wildest dreams). Things like this simply did not happen to me! The 15 minutes with the doctor had been so full of startling revelations that my head was buzzing fit to bust. Thoughts and feelings were fizzing together in a frenzy of expectation and unexpected delight. I was... I was... lost for words!! (Probably a first for me).

In this euphoric state I threw myself even more into the exercise programme, and by the start of July I was managing a total of:

- **37.5 minutes on the treadmill at 4.5% incline (Fast walk, obviously) – split into one lot of 20 minutes, and one of 17.5 minutes**
- **35 minutes on the bike but now up to resistance level 7 – 2 lots of 17.5 minutes**
- **20 minutes on the rowing machine at resistance level 5 - 2 lots of 5 and one of 10 minutes**

During this time Number Four was doing her GCSEs, and to make life easier for her she had been spending a few days mid-week at her mother's which was much closer to the school. I was still on a high from the visit to the doctor, and had come to the conclusion that I had earned myself some form of reward for all my hard work I had been investing in myself. For no apparent reason I was checking my diary and came to the realisation that I had absolutely nothing in it for the whole of the following week. This was a very rare state of affairs indeed. I racked my brains and simply could not remember the last time I had a completely empty diary for a whole week. Eventually I decided that it could only have been the last time that I had been on any sort of holiday, and that was a very long time ago.

Holiday!! What a brilliant idea. Why didn't I think of that?

You just did.

Shut up, I was going to say, if I hadn't been so rudely interrupted, why didn't I think of that BEFORE?

This was actually a Saturday morning, so I literally grabbed my jacket before I could change my mind, and headed straight into the city centre to find a travel agent. There was a choice of three, but I hit Thomas Cook and sat down next to the first, unoccupied consultant.

"I have a free week in my diary next week, so where am I going on holiday?"

You could see that old expression cross her face in a flash – that *why do I get all the nutters?* – resigned look.

"No, I'm deadly serious. I have a sudden unexpected opportunity to go on holiday for a week, and need to know what you have as last minute availabilities."

She visibly perked up, and kicked into gear with a string of all the right queries, such as how many people, how far away, did I want a city or beach resort and somewhere cold, warm or hot.

"What do you mean only one person?"

Travel agents, if not the whole holiday travel business, are completely thrown when you want to holiday alone. Everything is designed for two people sharing or as a family package, and as soon as you mention the words single traveller, the rate book goes out the window and in comes the travel agents guide to how much you can surcharge sad loners. Once I had got the message through to her that I only wanted to know what it was going to cost me, not what it might have cost if two had been going, we could start to get somewhere on a list of choices. Within half an hour I found that I had bought and paid for 8 days self catering in a beach side apartment in Stalida, Crete, leaving on Monday evening from Gatwick. I now had 48 hours to acquire suitable clothing for a holiday (jogging bottoms and sweatshirts were simply not going to cut it in the Greek Islands), get some currency and travellers cheques, buy suntan lotion, tell people what I was doing, pack and get to Gatwick Airport. No problem.

To their credit, the girls thought it was a wonderful idea, and greeted the plan with enthusiasm. It didn't take me long to realise that Number Four's particular enthusiasm was largely based on the realisation that she would have the flat to herself for the following weekend, and plenty of mates to keep her company, but I decided I could trust her. The shopping could be a problem though, and it was going to force me to break with my master plan of not buying too much in the way of clothes while I was still losing weight. Then I realised that I would be heading for Spain with the boys in October, and anything I bought now, provided I kept it all on the reasonably tight but still comfortable side would have a dual purpose anyway. This depended upon finding a shop that would sell clothes my size, and I knew that this would be a problem from years of experience. I headed in to the shops on the Sunday, and thought I would at least start with a success and get some underwear. The first shop I came to with men's clothes was M&S, so in I went to buy some socks – never a problem. It got interesting when I spotted some light linen trousers which looked particularly suited to mediterranean climes, and I thought

Why not at least try on the largest pair and see how close you are to getting there.

The little beauties only *fitted me*! WOW! I was actually buying *real* clothes off the peg in a major high street store, not just sports kit this time – a blinding vision of a whole new world spread out before me. Who cares about the Road to Damascus – give me the first floor of M&S every time! I was like a pig in a swamp – Charlie in the Chocolate Factory. I was surrounded by endless racks of clothes of all shapes and styles and colours and I could have any of them I wanted.

Then it struck me like a bolt of lightning. I didn't really have a single clue what I did want. I didn't know what colours were good or bad on me, what sort of style would suit me, and worse, I hadn't even thought about what I actually needed for the trip. It dawned on me that I had actually gone out shopping for clothes in the full expectation of having virtually no choice at all, and doing what came naturally, buying what little I could find to fit me, if anything. This was a whole new ballgame, and I had not the slightest notion of the rules. So I made my mental excuses and left empty-handed, wandering immediately down to my local Italian café and taking solace in a large cappuccino. Deflated, and at a loss as to how to proceed, I nursed my coffee and watched the world walk by. This was not me – I didn't do *cop-outs*! *Pull yourself together*.

OK, let's start by working out what I physically need for the trip, how many pairs of trousers? Trousers! I'm more likely to need shorts in Crete in July. Good decision. I'm only going for 8 days, more like 6 on the ground, so I'll probably get away with two of each. The list gradually grew to a small yet manageable and practical list to get me through the week. As I compiled this mental list, I was beginning to take extra notice of the passing shoppers and again coming to the realisation that it didn't really matter what styles or colours I bought as I had two major advantages firmly and securely on my side. Firstly, everybody in the developed world knows, without fear of contradiction, that the British male on holiday in warm countries has zero dress sense. Secondly, I would know nobody in Stalida, and nobody in Stalida would know me. Therefore it didn't matter what I bought and wore, as long as it kept me cool and decent during the day, and warm enough at night.

I had another cappuccino, smiled wryly to myself, gathered my wits about me, and went shopping. It had been a close call there for a moment or two, but I finally returned home with a holiday wardrobe ready to wear, whipped all the labels off, packed everything except what I would be travelling in, and breathed a huge sigh of relief. Why did life always have to introduce complications just when you thought you were getting on top of it? Anyway, I'd faced that moment today and won through, and here I was all packed and ready for the off. I could sleep easily tonight, and this time tomorrow I'd be heading for the beaches of the Greek Islands, swimming in the warmth of the…

Swimming trunks – you haven't got any swimming trunks.

Sleeping went right out of the window. I sat up and went through every possible set of circumstances, every usual holiday activity and checked off everything I might need to see if I possessed it and had packed it. As luck would have it, swimming trunks were indeed the only missing item, and that could be easily resolved in the morning long before I would have to leave. Finally, and considerably later than planned, I did get to bed and slept soundly, content that I was fully prepared to enjoy myself.

At Gatwick, I seriously began to wonder whether I had committed one of the all time great foul-ups. Waiting at the departure gate to board the plane it was obvious that I was the oldest passenger by a margin of something approaching 30 years. To think that I could have been worried about what I would wear had been filed under ridiculous, and I was starting to imagine that these folk would all be heading for my apartment building. I finally deduced that the flight was full of a combination of kids having an *A Levels are finished let's all go and get drunk in the sun* holiday, and a motley collection of stag parties, hen parties and folks who had abandoned Club 18-30 because it was too formal and didn't allow enough drinking and sex, and me. The flight itself was everything I had by then come to expect, and the cabin staff seemed to react as if it was all entirely natural. On arrival in Crete I made my way to the appointed welcome desk, and was relieved beyond belief that only three of us went that way. The young man handed us some envelopes, explained that as we were the only ones going to Stalida, he had organised taxis rather than a bus. Things were looking up. An extremely scary and very fast taxi ride later through the unlit Cretan night and I was dropped off outside my apartment building and the taxi was gone. Two hours later – after thanking the powers that be that I had not left my mobile phone at home; having crossed over the road to get a signal so that I could contact the emergency number in the envelope I had been handed at the airport; after sitting on my suitcase on the side of a dark silent street; two reps turned up with a key and let me into my room. To this day, and after numerous letters, I have never received a proper apology from Thomas Cook, and to my dying day they will never receive any further business from me. It beggars belief as to what might have happened if the holiday-maker had been a single girl, without a mobile phone! Unforgivable!

The morning came, and I was at last able to explore what had been described as a 'front line apartment block with beachside bar'. My first-floor apartment actually overlooked the high street, and the beachside bar actually belonged to another apartment block which really was front line, and which I could use if I showed my key. Who cares, I decided, I came here to enjoy myself, not to moan. I wasn't going to sit in my room or hang around a bar anyway.

The good news was that I had landed smack in the middle of a scorching heat wave, and almost every bar in town was showing the World Cup quarter and semi-finals courtesy of various satellite TV stations from different countries. The bad news was that this not so long ago charming, little, *off the beaten track* Greek town now sported burger bars, pizza houses, Chinese, Indian and Italian restaurants, a Rovers Return pub complete with quiz night on Tuesdays and Thursdays, a Queen Vic pub with its quiz nights on Mondays and Wednesdays, but sadly only one small Greek Taverna and one Greek restaurant.

I soon found my way around the place, and learned to avoid the flying quad bikes that were hired from two places in the town and were the transport of choice for overloaded parties to progress from one bar to the next. I quickly discovered the beautiful sandy beach, the quiet out of the way bars and cafés, and a large bar right on the beach at the far end of the high street from the main bars and clubs. This was a very large open air bar with the most comfortable chairs in town, a discreet Greek barman and a very laid-back DJ (without a microphone) whose main role was to ensure an unbroken very light background of classic jazz and blues. The tables were presided over by a Greek goddess, who floated regally between them dispensing nectar, (straight from the mouth of a Metaxa brandy bottle, in my case), to her late night flock. The coffee wasn't bad there either.

This week was a breath of fresh air (and not just the sea air either). It made me realise after a day or so that there are times when you should just switch off, not from work or anything as mundane as that. I mean switch off, right from the heart outwards. Forget the rules, forget the formalities, the expectations others have of you, and just go with the flow of whatever happens without judging. This has since become another of my little rules, which I often try to pass on to anyone who will listen, especially anyone struggling with a diet or weight loss. I sum it up as:

Don't forget to feed the soul too!

When we push ourselves too hard on diets, and when we absolutely deny ourselves anything which is no longer good for us, we either give up completely because we can't take the pressure any more, or fall to the wayside and binge on forbidden fruits and then feel guilty for weeks afterwards. More dieters have failed because they have forgotten to feed their souls than for any other reason. Feeding your soul is not falling off the wagon; it is not failing, it is not abandoning hope or a breakdown of willpower. It is a cold, calm, deliberate acknowledgement of the fact that many things which we now know to be bad for our health, or bad for our diet, or bring us out in spots or whatever your worst nightmare might actually be, are actually deeply enjoyable, and make life a little bit easier to bear. Feeding your soul is the recognition that life will be severely, if not terminally, diminished to the point of not being bearable, if every single one of these little pleasures is never to be experienced again. What is life worth without a little fun from time to time?

That week in Crete I fed my soul. *I had a mixed grill for breakfast in the Robin Hood*, run by a charming couple from Nottingham, an Indian meal, a Chinese meal, a few beers watching the football, and every night coffees and brandies brought to me by Sophia (we had by now been formally introduced by the barman) in the beach bar till extremely late. It was extremely easy to do this for the week, as there was the additional distance from normality to reinforce the freedom, and the return home would strongly reinforce the return to the regular regime.

About half way through the week I stumbled upon another piece of evidence about my new shape. Somehow I had fallen into a conversation, during a match on the TV in a bar, with a young guy who was on his own on holiday from Bradford. He worked, if I remember correctly, for a supermarket bakery. We were discussing places we had eaten in the town, and he had clearly not tried any of the beach restaurants, or either of the two Greek places. He preferred to eat pizza or Indian every night as he might not like the local food. At this point I swept my cloak of many colours of fatherhood around my shoulders with a flourish and proceeded to give him both barrels on why he should never pass up the opportunity to try something for the first time if it was offered, as he might just end up liking it. Why he should never visit a place for the first time and not try the local food and drink for precisely the same reason. To his credit, he calmly sat there and took it all in, probably out of courtesy as I had just bought the last round! I then wandered off down to the other end of town, and had a coffee in a little restaurant overlooking the broad sweep of the next bay. As I sat in the warm afternoon sun reading a book, I noticed that someone was parascending across the bay. At least, I think that's what it's called when you are towed behind a speedboat dangling beneath a parachute in a harness. I casually thought to myself that I had seen this in quite a few places over the years, and wondered what it was like, it looked like fun. Of course, I had never even considered it. Given my weight and dimensions I would probably not fit in the harness anyway.

Suddenly I sat bolt upright. Hadn't I just berated that poor baker's lad from Bradford for what seemed like hours on the follies of never trying something new? Hadn't I just pleaded with him never to turn down the chance to try something for the first time? I finished my coffee and headed straight down the beach to the water sports tent.

"Excuse me. I'd like to have a turn in that parachute thing, please."

The Mancunian with bleached hair, who was trying to give the impression of still being young and failing miserably, turned out to be in charge. He calmly told me:

"Not dressed like that, mate. You need to change into swimming gear for that. And don't you think you're a bit old for that anyway?"

Down boy! You came for a parachute ride, not a slanging match!

"If you're young enough to be a beach bum, then I'm young enough to ride that chute'"

He grinned, "Off you go and get your trunks; we'll be here for hours yet. And don't forget your camera. The grandkids'll want photos of this!"

"Cheeky sod!"

I was on a mission now. I went straight back to change, and yes, I grabbed the camera because *I* wanted photos of this one! I went off down to the beach again, with a fair amount of cash as I thought it might prove to be an expensive ride, and I had completely forgotten to ask. In a few moments we were off out into the bay and I was being strapped in for the ride of my life. I'm certain that our little exchanges of banter had brightened his day from the normal run of kids hanging around, as instead of the studiously observed route of the previous flights I had witnessed we seemed to cover the full length of the bay, and I had the pleasure of a second lap. With a casual flick of the throttles he twice took me from the highest extension of the tow cable, with magnificent views, swooping down to gently drag my feet through the water before returning skyward.

I had now shed another bit of the old me. That part which had known for too long that my size and shape denied me the chance or the ability to do so many things through life. This part had watched the kids on the extreme rides at Alton Towers knowing that the safety bars would not close if I sat with them, that even if I could squeeze myself in my heart would probably not take it, and that I had been turned away from too many rides and bumper cars in so many fairgrounds because of my size to risk being further embarrassed. Those days were gone. My friendly beach bum had seen to that by simply looking at my age compared to his normal customers, and never seeing a weight or size problem. It was time to readjust the mental image and accept that I wasn't like that any more.

I went back to that same restaurant where I had spotted the parachute that afternoon, and had the top of the range seafood platter for dinner, whilst gazing out over the scene of another victory. Life really was getting its fun side back!

The week drew on, and I discovered The Tee Shirt Factory where they could print anything you wanted onto a T-shirt in next to no time while you waited. They had a vast catalogue of designs, and any lettering you could dream up. Two or three graphic designs of sayings caught my eye, and I acquired two shirts saying *When I read about the evils of drinking I gave up . . . reading and At my age I've – seen it all, done it all, heard it all – I just can't remember it all.* These were just impulse buys, but have caused a lot of fun over the last year or two. The main reason I went in there in the first place was to get a plain shirt with the letters TISM across the front of the chest. I thought it would be fun to have this for the trip to Spain with the boys, as my nickname had now officially become *The Incredible Shrinking Man*.

All good things must come to an end, and with my soul having been fed to bursting point, (and on at least one night having had slightly too much Metaxa), it was time to board the plane home. At the airport I was re-united with my fellow passengers from the outward trip, who were showing all the classic symptoms of having had their perfect holiday too. Mostly they were sitting with different people, looking very hung-over, and covered with bright red sunburn which would probably keep them awake at night for days back home even though they largely slept the whole flight back.

A day later, well rested, full of contentment on the inside, and resembling polished mahogany on the outside, I hit the gym again in a white T-shirt (well, when you get the chance, you've got to take it). The soul had been fed – now the body must pay the bill!

CHAPTER SEVEN

LOOSE SKIN

FRESH BACK FROM MY WEEK IN CRETE - BRONZED, BURNISHED AND WITH THE soul still purring, I deliberately had not weighed myself since returning from holiday, as it would serve no purpose other than creating negative feelings. I knew I would probably have put on a few pounds, but I knew equally that I could get rid of it within a few weeks just by returning to *business as usual*.

As soon as I walked onto the gym floor I discovered that my fitness instructor, with whom I often had a chat about progress, had left. It was also time for my six week review and programme update. The main question then was who would now take responsibility for my programme? It fell to a guy called Mickey, who I had not actually met on any of my previous visits. He turned out to be quite a character as he put me through the full introductory question and answer session again so that he could really appreciate what I wanted to achieve. Of course he insisted on weighing me, and jumped immediately to the conclusion that I hadn't been putting enough effort in as I hadn't got close to losing anything. My protestations about being on holiday, backed up with all the obvious evidence in front of his eyes, fell on completely deaf ears (even though he had a grin when he said it), and he proceeded to introduce me to a small group of resistance machines and something loosely based, I thought, on a medieval torture rack. My new programme now consisted of three to four sessions per week of:

- **Burn 150 calories on the treadmill** as fast as I could (the machine worked out the calories and showed them on a screen)
- **Burn 150 calories on the bike**

- **Burn 150 calories on the x-trainer** (a sort of cross-country skiing machine, arms and legs all pumping away at once)
- **Chest press** – three sets of 16 presses (push a handle attached to some weights away from your chest)
- **Lateral pull downs** three sets of 16 (pull down a bar above your head – weights attached again)
- **Leg press** three sets of 16 (sit down and push a pad away from you with your legs – and yes, there were weights attached)
- **Shoulder press** three sets of 16 (this time push a bar up above your head)
- **Chin-ups and dips** (a weird machine where you stood on a bar while doing them, and the weights made it easier by supporting some of your own weight)
- **Finish on a mat on the floor** with one of those strange *roll cage* things which are designed to improve your abdominal muscles (six pack!)

Apparently the idea was that when you could manage to do all three sets of 16 on a machine, then you made a note and increased the weight a notch next time. It took me a few sessions to be able to find the right machines without help, and to remember how to use each one properly. But before long I had got myself into the habit of not being satisfied unless I could tick off a weight progression on at least one machine every time I went to the gym.

This new routine didn't really save any time, but it certainly re-introduced me to muscles which had long lain dormant, if not totally atrophied. Curiously, it was also a much more sociable routine. The treadmills, bikes and x-trainers tended to be lined up in rows, or round the outside of the gym and each had its own TV set where you could select your channel and plug in your headphones – totally anti-social. On the other hand the resistance machines were squeezed randomly into the middle of the gym area, all fairly close together, and each requiring short rest periods between sets which almost inevitably ended in conversations breaking out spontaneously with whoever was sat on the adjacent machines. To counter this, they were also right in front of the gym desk, and Mickey would often wander over and check my workout diary, and check the weight settings I was using. He quickly came to realise that I was serious, and never needed to hassle me about progressing.

The high point of the month was a trip to Portsmouth for Number Two's graduation, a completely new experience as I had never been near such a ceremony before. I had not even come close to going to university myself, and Number One had fallen into a dispute over her choice of dissertation subject with her tutor at LIPA and opted to accept a diploma rather than compromise. So a great couple of days down on the coast were had by all concerned, and the proud Dad got ritually ripped off and loved every minute of it. Behind the scenes and the sunglasses, my emotions served as a powerful reminder of what I was now doing, and why I was doing it. Moments like this were *once in a lifetime*, and I had been so close to missing them it almost didn't bear thinking about.

Before I knew it the monthly check-up was here, and I realised that I had been so busy catching up on work issues, and enjoying the new gym routines, that I really hadn't thought much about moving the eating programme along a bit as well. So it came as no surprise to find that I had only lost a single pound that month. I was not too bothered, to be honest, but my doctor was happy that I had been on a good holiday, relaxed on all fronts, ignored the diet while I was away, and still ended the month with a small weight loss. When he put it like that, who was I to disagree! The other vital signs were all making progress as well, so we both smiled and off I went.

August drifted by on a tide of complacency, if the truth be analysed now. The diet was stable and working well, so I had long since stopped taking the tablets as they were no longing producing any discernable effect, although I admit that I had not yet told my doctor. The programme at the gym was progressing nicely and the sun was shining as and when it should. The girls were working their way through the usual succession of boyfriends, or *latest victims* as I quite openly called them! I tried, as ever, to be as non-judgemental as possible, accepting all comers in the roles, and as ever was accused of being *nice* to them because I would have *preferred* to have had sons rather than daughters. It is totally impossible to win this argument, so, as ever, I smiled and kept quiet.

The complacency became fixed into place with the advance notice of an appointment with the reconstructive surgery team for the end of September, and the August weigh-in with Dr Ken showed 15 stone 3 lb, a loss of well over 12¼ stone now. What was there possibly to be concerned about? For the first time, since I literally could not remember when, I was happy. Not only that, I was feeling fit, getting great regular exercise and eating well. I was looking good with the tan hanging on well and bits of the body that had been a bit slack were starting to firm up well with the new programme. I had a holiday with the boys coming up in October, and now the surgeon was going to remove the stomach *hangover* (which would also lose a pound or two more). What more could a guy want?

In mid September Mickey announced that it was now time to review the programme again. He knew, by now, that I had an appointment with the surgeon, and he had also finally come to terms with just how much weight I had lost. His decision was to devise a new schedule designed to tone up all the various little saggy bits around my body that were showing up through the weight loss, so that when the surgeon *did* my stomach, the rest would not lag behind and let me down. The point was that it was entirely up to me; he was not going to stand over me and shout at me, but just tell me what would work if I wanted to give it a go. Ultimately, it was nothing to do with him whether I bothered or not.

This time, he had given it considerable thought, and used all his expertise to put together a great set of exercises which I had to do in the exact order he set out. Apparently each group of machines, if used in the right order, would have a combined cumulative effect on different muscle groups. This was all rocket science to me now, way outside of my limited knowledge, so I nodded my head, learnt how to use the new machines, and wandered off to the steam room to give my brain a rest. Sometimes I worried about Mickey – if he wasn't trying to storm the barriers of new pain levels for his charges, he was messing with our brains by presenting little conundrums to solve, or performing card tricks at the gym desk. To be fair, his own personal workouts were pretty awesome, at least till he went too far one day and damaged his back! It was about this time that I started mentally referring to him as *Masochistic Mickey*, although to this day I've never let him know that.

The new complacency and the new gym programme did not make good bed-fellows, so for a while the gym did not actually see me putting in quite the usual level of effort. I realised that I had never actually set a target weight, and nor had the doctor. I would never have believed that I could possibly lose as much as I had anyway, so I felt that, theoretically, I could already claim to have met my target. I did not change my eating habits, as I was perfectly content with what I was eating, and didn't have any mad cravings anymore. I could walk pass a hot dog stand, an ice cream vendor or a burger bar without a second thought. I had reached where I wanted to be, and with the impending surgery I would finally be able to draw a line under this whole extraordinary story. I enjoyed the gym; I enjoyed the exercise and the banter there, so I kept going along and working through my sessions, but there didn't seem to be the urgent need to keep pushing things to the limits with the weights, or hitting the calorie targets on the cardiovascular machines quicker all the time.

September's check up revealed a loss of another few pounds, and I was now below the 15 stone level, with the loss topping 12½ stone. No problem. What else would you expect?

At last the 29th arrived, and I arrived at Clinic G just a little early for my visit to Mr Malata. My name was called, and in I went. After reviewing my notes, he told me he thought that what I had achieved was probably the best weight loss story he had ever personally seen. He had a good look at the overhanging skin, and told me that it would be absolutely no problem to remove this, and would be a pleasure. He had a look at the insides of my thighs, and asked if I thought they needed doing as well. There wasn't much in the way of loose skin there, so I told him I didn't think so. He told me about the operation he would do, and then sent me along the corridor to have the clinical photography guys get some photos for the medical records.

I was feeling absolutely on top of the world now, and had a few laughs with the photographer who also said that he had seen nothing like it before, and had certainly photographed nothing like it before. After the photos I had to go back to the consulting rooms and one of the nurses measured me in various directions and checked my weight, pulse and blood pressure. Then I went back in for another chat with the main man. He asked me if I would have any objection to him using my photos and notes for teaching purposes, as he was based at Addenbrookes Hospital which is more or less the medical side of Cambridge University. No problem, if he was prepared to put his skills to work for me, then it was the least I could do. I was reaching quite a state of excitement by now, as this would finally be the culmination of the whole project, I could actually wrap it up and move on. Everything was set, and so I asked the only remaining question.

"When will you actually do it?"

"As soon as possible."

"Is there a waiting list for this sort of operation, and how long is it?"

"Not really for this, but we do have a waiting list for the surgical team. We'll put you on the waiting list as soon as we can."

"I'm sorry, what do you mean, as soon as you can?"

"We can only put you on the list when your body mass index (BMI) is down to 27. It used to be 29, but the Primary Care Trust (the local board in charge of the National Health Service in the area) has changed the rules recently. You have to be 27 or below. Go with the nurse now and she will work it all out for you. I'll see you again as soon as you hit 27."

Slightly bemused by this sudden turn of events, I went with the nurse to see what weight I would have to be to hit this magic number. She shot me down in flames by telling me I would have to lose another 2 stone.

"TWO STONE! Don't be ridiculous. I can't possibly lose another two stone. I've already lost 13 stone; I can't possibly have that much fat left to lose."

"Sorry, love. Them's the rules."

"I might as well forget the whole thing."

Completely deflated, I wandered back to the car and headed home. I'd been set up beautifully, and then knocked back so hard it hurt. I didn't know what to say or do that whole weekend, I was just numb. I knew with an absolute certainty that I really could never even contemplate losing another two whole stone. The whole journey had been long and hard, and now I was stuck with this loose skin flopping about below my waist. Why on earth did they let me think the surgery was possible? It was a cruel, nasty, vicious and completely unnecessary act of unpardonable wickedness. I got quite angry in the end, which didn't do a whole lot of good but might have lightened the burden just a little.

The whole of the next week I was pretty much like a bear with a sore head. I did actually manage to go the gym and put in my normal sessions, but more just to keep to some sort of a routine as I searched for the way forward. I eventually calmed myself down enough to think a little straighter, and concentrated on getting things together for the trip to Spain with the boys. At least I could buy myself a few more bits for the holiday, as I knew now what size I was going to be for the foreseeable future. I needed a few more things than I had taken to Crete, as I had originally decided, when booking the flights months ago, that I would actually stay on in Spain for an extra few days just to get a quiet break all to myself before the winter set in. This had been before the spur of the moment Crete trip, so amounted to a bit of a luxury now, but it was bought and paid for already so never mind, just enjoy it.

The flights to Spain had co-ordinated fairly well, with my Gatwick flight getting in first, followed an hour or so later by the Glasgow flight hopefully with The Auld Git aboard. He had originally acquired the nickname when his daughter was expecting her first child, the arrival of which would turn him into a grandfather. Hence he became a grand-father-in-training, a GIT - it had just never gone away. So I had just an hour to kill in the arrivals hall in Malaga Airport, and get quickly accustomed to the fabulous dry heat. I had put the setback out of my mind, and was determined to enjoy myself. I was even wearing my *TISM* T-shirt, especially made for me in Crete, which I thought the boys might like. The others were due to arrive from Edinburgh a few hours later, so the advance party would simply find a bar to wait in.

As I stood waiting by the exit from the customs area, I spotted The Auld Git making his way through. Although we kept in touch regularly by emails, I realised it had been almost a year since I had last seen him at the FRA Christmas lunch in Edinburgh. It was now October, and I allowed myself a wry, self-satisfied smile as he walked up to me, looked straight at me for a second, blanked me completely and headed straight on past. Enjoying myself immensely now, I manoeuvred carefully around the café and bar area, making sure that every minute or two he had to look straight at me again, and detour to get past me. Eventually, he extracted his mobile phone, and made the agreed call if we failed to spot each other when he arrived.

As my phone rang, I stood about four feet in front of him, and enquired why he thought it necessary to use a phone when I was stood right in front of him? His face was an absolute picture. Even for a Scot, straight off the flight from Glasgow, his grasp of old fashioned Anglo-Saxon was impressive. I needed to start getting used to this reaction – even my best old friends no longer recognised me.

A similar reaction occurred once the others arrived on the Edinburgh flight, although it was slightly easier for them as they at least recognised one of us and therefore me more by association than anything else. The week quickly degenerated, as we decided to drop in an old member of the gang who was now living out there permanently, just a short detour off the motorway on our way to Marina Duquesa where the trips were based nowadays. Suffice to say that during our supposedly brief stop it became unwise (drinking and driving don't mix) for us to complete the trip down the coast later on as planned, so we didn't actually make it to the apartment till the following day. The rest of that week falls firmly behind the cloak of the golden rule – *What goes on in Spain, stays in Spain.*

Seven days later I bade farewell to the guys as they caught their flights back to Scotland, and grabbed a taxi for the short hop to the hotel I had booked for the next six nights on the front at Torremolinos. I had picked up a good deal on the internet, and it was a pleasant, but pricey place, just a bit off the beaten track. It was just what I needed, a quiet few days of solitude to ponder what the surgeon had said.

Unfortunately, or maybe, with 20:20 hindsight, fortunately, I got exactly that. A quiet few days of solitude; a quiet few days spent wandering aimlessly up and down the extremely long esplanade, with only myself for company, where the highlights were getting the paper and completing the crossword over a coffee in a different café each day and trying to find restaurants for dinner that didn't object to having to give up a precious table for just a single diner.

In the end I was desperate to get out of there and get home. The day of my flight simply couldn't come quickly enough. I came face to face, during those few days, with the realisation that there was still a lot of work to bring everything to a proper conclusion. I was very far from being a finished project, as much mentally as physically. I needed to get home and put things in order. I needed to find a purpose, a new target, something to aim at. At that moment I was effectively a rudderless ship, with no destination, no cargo to deliver and without any navigation system. If I thought I was a finished project I was totally delusional – I was actually a blank canvas in dire need of inspiration.

As soon as the flight had come and rescued me, I immediately made an appointment to see Dr Ken a few days earlier that month. Unsurprisingly I had put on a few pounds while away and was back to 15¼ stone, but the heart rate and blood pressure were both fine. I told him all about the visit to the consultant, and how he was totally unreasonable in expecting me to get below 13 stone. I still don't fully understand how he did it, but a few minutes later I left with the absolute certainty that my next target was 13 stone, and that I *would* do it. As far as I can recall, he reminded me that I had already lost more weight than he would have ever have believed possible, told me that I looked and obviously felt fitter than I had probably ever been and that as far as he could tell, from the comfort of his surgery, I probably hadn't even broken sweat over it yet and had just treated it as an experiment in the art of the possible. He got me to believe that I could achieve that weight loss, and sent me back out on a mission again.

How did he do that? – The man's a genius.

CHAPTER EIGHT

AN ACTUAL TARGET

SO OCTOBER 2006 FINDS ME AT 15¼ STONE, WITH A TARGET OF A BODY MASS index of 27, meaning I had to get down to around 13 stone. But a target of *around something* is no target, so I decided I'd better set an actual target, something defined, something I could almost touch and feel. That's when I remembered that magic number from somewhere way back in my school days. The only weight that ever stuck in my memory – 12 stone 12 pounds. It would be astounding if I could actually get back to the weight I was when I was at school, and it wasn't that far under the target of BMI 27, so that was it. New target acquired, I *would* be 12 stone 12 lbs.

That was the easy bit – now how on earth would I get there? Well I had that fancy technical programme set up by Masochistic Mickey, so that would be a good start, and I could take a new look at my eating habits, and between those two it should do the trick.

But what if it isn't enough? What if I don't make the target?

Oh, shut up! The incentive of the surgery is too good to miss, and I'd better get on with it or they'll change the rule to something more ridiculous like 25 or 23 BMI!

So I got stuck into the new gym programme and started to learn my way around the new strange and wonderful machines, and quickly regained the mental need to tick off at least one *progression* (move up to the next weights level) every time I ran through the programme.

This is the programme that I followed that winter:

1. **Warm up on rowing machine** – 1000 metres at level six (try to do it quicker each time).

2. **Fast walk on the treadmil.** 15 minutes.
3. **Chest press.** 75kg. To failure. (This means you try to do 16 repetitions in one go, but to begin with you might 'fail' at less than 16. When you can do 16 in an unbroken sequence, then next time you increase the weight.)
4. **Squat press.** Set of 16.
5. **Lateral pulldown.** 115kg. To failure.
6. **Step up and bicep curl.** (Bench step ups, with 8kg in each hand. On each step up, raise the weight from the elbow) 16 left leg, 16 right leg.
7. **Hamstring curls.** 60kg. to failure. (This is a ghastly machine where you lie on your front, hook the weight bar behind your ankles and then bend your knees to raise the weight bar.)
8. **Exercise Bike.** 15 minutes at level 17.

Then repeat exercises 3 to 8.

9. **Cross-trainer.** 15 minutes at level 13.
10. **Abdominal twists.** 16 to right, 16 to left (alternating).
11. **Sit-ups on a fit-ball.** 16.

This one is not for the faint-hearted, and should not be attempted as a beginner routine at all. It is actually an intensive routine that works the body from head to foot without getting too specific in any areas. A session lasted between 90 minutes and two hours and on average I completed this programme every second day.

THE OTHER STEP I NEEDED TO TAKE WAS THE LOOK AT THE EATING AGAIN, and work out what improvements I could make on that front. The only way I was going to make any real progress on this front was by trying to learn a bit more about the subject, and so I started to wander around the internet looking for a useful website that would contain the sort of information I was really after. This turned out to be an odyssey of truly epic proportions, because there is more stuff out there on this subject than any person could possibly read in a lifetime of total dedication. But one thing became abundantly clear in next to no time – whatever advice was given by any really authoritative source on any aspect of the subject, you could be sure to find a dozen other equally good sources that told you the exact opposite! Who on earth did you trust on this stuff? Especially true was the fact that if you found a good-looking site that seemed to give an honest personal experience, it would always turn out to be *sponsored* by some organisation or other trying to sell you some magic potion, therapy programme, or branded range of products of one sort or another. A very large number of sites actually required you to join and pay a subscription fee!

Clearly I was going to get nowhere here, or waste the rest of my life trying to find the perfect source of information, so it was going to be a simple case of going back to my tried and tested habit of *trial and error*. I would have to experiment and see what worked for me, and what didn't. The only problem with this was that it took ages, and you could only deal with one aspect at a time or you couldn't tell what worked and what didn't work. It also had the distinct disadvantage of not determining whether any of the things would work well in combination. But let's face it, I didn't have any other option, so I decided to stop whining and get on with it!

And stopping whining and getting on with it was clearly working, as the November session with my doctor revealed that I was now 14½ stone – a brand new record for the programme. This was all I needed to keep me at it with a vengeance. After all, it had only been a few weeks back that I had thought it was more or less impossible to lose any more weight, yet here was another ¾ of a stone gone!

Towards the end of that November the national chain of gyms, to which mine belonged, introduced a little fun idea for the Christmas and New Year period, which I completely ignored, initially. The *Calorie Count Challenge* was a competition where the gym staff tried to sign up as many members as possible to record the calories they burnt in their programmes in the gym. The basic idea was to encourage members to try to burn off the excess calories they would surely consume through the festive food and drink binge. Each member who recorded over 3,000 calories burnt would get a free t-shirt, there would be a prize draw, and a prize for the top lady and top gent *burner* in each club, and a national league table of all the clubs across the country. The whole thing was supposed to run from 1st December to 31st January. As I said, initially I just ignored this as a *typical* promotional thing, and just got on with my programme, but the week before it all kicked off I was finally persuaded by one of the guys there to sign up, mainly to stop them bothering me each time I showed up.

Now the human body is a complex and wonderful development of evolution and probably would never have become what it is today if it had relied on scientists and creative people to design it. But one particular trick it has up its sleeve always fascinates me, and has been a wonderful assistant in all my little exercise programmes. When you put the body through a really good exercise programme (or a good long run, as I later found out), one that is hard enough to really improve the body's efficiency, it rewards you by producing a special little set of chemicals called endorphins. Now I'm no scientist, and I'm not going to even attempt to explain what this all about, but these endorphins are the body's own special *feel good* drugs – a sort of personal reward for good behaviour designed to make you literally feel great when you exercise, and to make you feel like doing that again sometime soon.

My programme had by now reached the sort of intensity that was regularly producing these things, and I had begun to both enjoy and feel good about running through the full set and ticking off some progressions. The simple fact was that I was probably going to the gym something like four or five times a week, and even found myself popping in at the end of the day (even on rest days) just for a relaxing steam room and Jacuzzi. It was quite strange to be able to actually devote this sort of time exclusively to me, and as far as I was concerned there was absolutely nothing wrong with this at all.

The net result of this *frequent flyer* programme was that when the 1st December came along, and the Calorie Count Challenge got under way, rather than hoping to get the T-shirt in the eight week period, like most of the members, I astonished everyone (myself included) by getting it in the first week! Yes, that's right, I burned the requisite 3,000 calories in the first six days, and I had done nothing out of the ordinary because of the challenge, simply recorded my sessions on the sheet as instructed. I think this may have made some of the gym staff sit up and take a bit more notice of my activities. As a side effect I noticed that on most occasions when I wandered into the gym, one or other of the team there would be introducing me specifically to another new member. I didn't take much notice of this at first, putting it down to the usual thing of making new people welcome, but I quickly came to realise that I was being drawn into conversations, and frequently asked about my weight loss. Without realising, I had become the gym's *living proof* that you *can* lose a lot of weight if you use the gym properly and eat well. I didn't mind, hardly really gave it a second thought – if they wanted people to think the weight loss was down to their gym then let them. It was no skin off my nose and didn't take up too much time. I even got to meet some very pleasant people too!

Before I knew it, the 19th of December was beckoning, the Tuesday before Christmas. This is, by tradition, is the day for the FRA Christmas lunch, and I had booked my train tickets and hotel room some time before. Hotels are not a problem in Edinburgh at that time of year, but as ever, if you don't book your train journey months in advance it costs an absolutely outrageous amount of money to get there. It can be a lot cheaper to fly, but this is only an illusion as I would have had to take a train to get to an airport (there goes most of the cost saving), and the transport into Edinburgh from the airport there is diabolical – you usually end up in a taxi (there goes the rest of the savings). I had long since discovered that, if you are careful, you can work out exactly when the timetables become available online and if you get in really quickly you get the best possible deals. Having the FRA lunch booked with the restaurant a year in advance made this possible, so I had been able to get myself a first class seat both ways for a fraction of the normal cost of a standard fare. This gave the added advantage of free wi-fi on the train in first class, so I could work on the way up, and free coffee, biscuits and water from the steward for the whole journey. So I had a very comfortable trip up on the afternoon before (I never trust the railway in the morning for this lunch – unmissable), and a quiet evening setting myself up for the rigours of the next day!

As usual I was the first one to arrive, and although the boys who had been to Spain in October had obviously recognised me, the guys who hadn't been able to go this year had a struggle to begin with. Let's face it, I'd lost another 4½ stone since I'd seen them last Christmas. We didn't realise until we went upstairs from the bar to the restaurant, but the place had changed hands since the previous year. It was now in the proud ownership of someone who had pretentions to master chef status (but appeared on that day to lack the talent which would have otherwise surely guaranteed it for him). Now I'm not going to claim that we are a collection of the most refined palates and experienced gourmets on the planet, but between us we have eaten in some fine establishments around the world from time to time (usually with a company paying) and know our way around the finer points of preparation and presentation of good food. Suffice to say that this was the last time we graced this establishment with our presence for the Christmas lunch.

This did not, I hasten to add, diminish the overall enjoyment of the occasion, and the not-insignificant quantity of good Rioja and port which seemed to disappear quite rapidly. In other words, with the exception of the actual meal itself, it was a perfectly normal FRA lunch. Tradition then dictates that the party moves gently along from one hostelry to another on a fixed route, the origins of which are lost in the mists of time (and hazy memories). Some years we don't quite manage to make the full route, which in extreme years finishes with a late curry down near Leith Docks. This year was one where we didn't quite make it. Perhaps age was creeping up on us and we were getting sensible, who knows? I made it back to the hotel in one piece, with the power of speech intact, and got a good night before the journey back the next day.

Christmas was now upon us, and had its own difficulties this year being the first Christmas that the girls had experienced anywhere other than the old house. I decided to settle for the compromise of a restaurant booking to avoid the problems associated with the girls choosing between lunch at Mum's or lunch at Dad's, and I really wanted to avoid any attempt at trying to recreate a *family* lunch. It wasn't a roaring success, too many scars and ghosts at the table, but we soon escaped and everyone came back to my flat for the inevitable Star Wars Monopoly and Texas Hold-em. At least the evening was a huge success as ever!

Finally the festive season drew to a close, and the momentous 2006 gave way gracefully to 2007, which tiptoed in coyly, giving no warning as to the changes it would bring. With the cupboards stripped of all the extras brought in for the girls and their boyfriends for Christmas, and the few bottles of good cheer remaining having been distributed according to taste, I quickly settled back into the routine of the gym programme, and trying to get a few more changes to my eating habits. Just as I was deciding on what my next experimental change might be, I spotted a notice up in the gym announcing that they were going to be running a new special course called the B Plan – an eight week weight management course to be taken by Adele and Martin two of the senior fitness team members. Apparently it was a new thing being trialled across the gym chain, and Adele and Martin had been on some course to set them up for it with the first 14 members signing up being enrolled on it for free. I thought about this for a few milliseconds and signed up! It was free and took place one night a week commencing at the end of the month. I had absolutely nothing to lose by doing it, and I thought I might even get some good ideas from it.

In the meantime, while waiting for the course to start, I got on with the gym programme. My first objective was to get rid of any extra I might have picked up over Christmas and New Year, followed by making a few more moves up the weight ladders on some of the machines. By the time the monthly check with my doctor came round I was at 14¼ stone. Although this was only a loss of ¼ stone since the November check, it did cover the FRA lunch trip, Christmas, my birthday and New Year, so still counted as a good result both as far as the doctor was concerned, and definitely as far as I was concerned. Let's face it, more loss is more loss, however you look at it.

Around this time, a chance comment made by one of the fitness team at the gym, introduced me to what has become a favourite principle of mine. I had achieved a good level of muscle tone with the programme I had been doing at the gym and had kept potential loose skin around the body to a virtual minimum. I had never even thought about the muscles being so much better than they had ever been in the past – and I'm not talking Mr Universe stuff here, just good honest everyday muscles where muscles ought to be. The principle was perfectly simple, muscle weighs more than fat. Perfectly obvious, once you think about it, but I had never even considered it in the slightest, so I could chalk this one up on the plus side, even though I had no idea how much it was worth in terms of actual weight. I also found out another intriguing and extremely positive principle – fat just sits there doing nothing of any merit, but muscle actually burns calories by its very nature, even when you are asleep. Now I had never, and will never, try to build muscle for the sake of it, unlike many folks who inhabit gyms and seem to spend more time looking in the mirrors than actually doing exercise or lifting weights. But it has to be said that this little gem of information meant that I was certainly not against acquiring a few along the way, just as a sort of by-product.

Around the middle of the month they announced that the Calorie Count Challenge was going to be concluded earlier than originally intended, but by then my sheet had found itself a new home somewhere, or gone on holiday, and as I had long since got my T-shirt I forgot about it entirely. Then one day the results were put up on a big display by the desk in the corner of the gym floor, and out of nothing more than idle curiosity I glanced at it to see who had won. I was totally shocked to find myself well inside the top 10 men on the list, and have wondered where I might have come if I had actually kept on recording my sessions for the last couple of weeks. Anyway, it was good to know, in some small way, that I was continuing to make a serious effort, as well as enjoying the results.

The first night of the *B Plan* course, on 31st January, revealed a mixed bag of participants, and, needless to say really, a predominance of the fairer sex. We were measured in all sorts of directions, and in some quite unexpected places, weighed and had our body fat percentages analysed. Everything was noted down in a way which would allow absolutely no excuses at the end of the course. Once we had been turned into a set of statistics, we had to write down the targets we hoped to achieve during the eight weeks. I wasn't the slightest bit concerned about specific measurements of biceps, or thighs, but I was obviously going to set myself a target on weight and with my new found knowledge I was also interested in my body fat percentage. According to my starting statistics, as they measured them, I weighed 14 stone 3.2 lbs, and my body fat was 22.8%, slightly above the maximum which was regarded as *normal* for me of 22%. So the targets that I set for myself for the course were a ½ stone weight loss, and a reduction of 3.5% in body fat.

For the first week we had to keep an honest diary of everything we ate and drank till the next session, and it's amazing how being totally honest actually helps you to cut back. Pure psychology, but it works a treat. We were also introduced to the concept of eating five times a day instead of three. Not an excuse to eat five meals, but a regime of breakfast, snack, lunch, snack, dinner, all nicely spaced out over the day. This keeps the metabolism working away, and also leaves you slightly less hungry at lunch and dinner. You don't end up eating more, but it helps the body to use what you do eat more effectively.

The other aim of the course was designed to get people using the gym equipment more effectively, and so the second session was spent in the gym itself, being instructed on the cardiovascular kit (treadmills, rowing machines and the like), and a number of the simpler resistance machines (basically weights on pulleys that you pulled or pushed in various directions). I kept a fairly low profile at this point as I was, by now, pretty well versed in everything they covered, and both the instructors knew it. Everyone was asked to pair up, and arrange to do a session or two together during the week, but luckily I was excused this as there was by now an odd number of participants due to an early drop-out. The bottom line, really, was that the programme I was doing in the gym would have scared the living daylights out of virtually everybody else on the course, and there was no point trying to team up with someone in the gym who wasn't on a similar programme.

During the first two or three weeks, apart from a lot of stuff which was blindingly obvious, one thing did stand out. This was the introduction to the Glycaemic Index, best known as being the basis of the *GI Diet*. At this point I will freely admit that I had indeed heard of the GI Diet, but had ignored it on the basis that I avoided all *plans*. I had also always thought it was some form of American thing designed by their Army for GIs. How dumb was that! Turned out that it was an index developed to help people with diabetes, and indicates roughly the speed that blood sugar levels rise after specific foods, and subsequently fall. The faster the blood sugar rises, the quicker it falls, so it is better for controlling blood sugar levels if you eat food that is low on the Glycaemic Index, as it raises the levels in a more controlled way, and maintains them for longer. The main point for dieters is that it is an indicator of the quality of the carbohydrates in food, and although you don't have to follow the specific *GI Diet*, it does give you a great indication of the comparative effects of different foods within groups.

So now I had a real list to use to compare the effects of different things I ate. The lower GI stuff tends to be wholegrain, less refined, and includes most fruit and veg. The benchmark suggested to us was that a value below 55 was better and above 55 was worse. Some of the scores on the lists we were provided with, were quite surprising, to say the least. Corn Flakes were 84 and Weetabix 83, yet oat porridge was 49 and All Bran 42. Similarly parsnips came in at 97, and carrots at 71, yet green beans are 48. Tomatoes are 15, whilst pineapple is 66, but plums are 24. To top it, orange juice was 56 versus apple juice at 41. This lesson was intriguing, and gave me a whole new way of looking at foods in terms of the contribution they were making to my energy levels during the day, and how much they would contribute to potential fat. What became clear to me was that if you ate foods that released their energy faster than you were going to use it up, you tended to try to store it as fat, but also felt the need for more food quicker as your blood sugar level would start to drop quicker. So the idea was to try to eat according to the planned activity following the meal. This course was already starting to pay for itself – although that was not hard as it was actually free.

By now the February check up was due, and I was feeling very positive. The exercise programme was progressing very smoothly, I was getting great input from the weight loss course, spring was about to be sprung on us, and I was feeling pretty good, to say the very least.

CHAPTER NINE

A CHANCE REMARK

IT HAD STARTED OUT SO NORMALLY, THAT TUESDAY MORNING IN FEBRUARY 2007, lulling me into a false sense of security. Just a plain ordinary day with my standard wake-up routine: have breakfast and do the post. I jumped into the car and headed off for my latest check with Dr Ken.

It would be *business as usual* with a weight check, heart rate, blood pressure, a brief chat and then away to let him get on with the serious business of treating sick people. My bit of news for him would be my performance in the Calorie Count Challenge at the gym. I thought that this would be something to report, just to prove I was still *on the case.*

Well *business as usual* it was, and the weight was down to a fraction over 13½ stone, almost ¾ stone down from January's weigh-in. He pronounced the right results on blood pressure and heart rate, and he seemed suitably impressed with the gym performance, but was obviously pre-occupied with something else, so I began to make my excuses and leave.

"Hold on, Mike, I want to say something."

This sounded just ever so slightly ominous, definitely not what you want to hear your doctor say, so I sat down again and pricked up my ears with not a little trepidation.

"OK, go for it then."

He dropped the *bomb.*

"I think you should do a run."

This little *group of seven* words don't exactly inspire the same awe, at first glance, as some other groups of seven! They don't inspire the same reaction as the Seven Wonders of the Ancient World. They don't have the same musical quality as Seven Brides for Seven Brothers, or the same sparkle as the Seven Sisters constellation. At that point I had no concept of the incredible impact that this little *group of seven* words would end up having on my entire lifestyle. In fact, on first encountering those seven words, put carefully together in that order, I dismissed them almost thoughtlessly:

"Don't be silly. I don't do running."

"No. I'm serious. I think you should do a run."

"I can't run. The skin hanging down from my stomach won't let me jog, it flops around too much."

"I definitely think it's time for you to consider doing a run."

I was clearly struggling here. *What could I say to get out of this? Throw some consequences back at him. Good thought!*

"If I end up doing a run, which I almost certainly won't, it will have to be for charity. And as it's your idea, it will cost you BIG TIME!"

But this was a sneaky guy I was dealing with here. He gave me the one response I really didn't want to hear.

"Fine then, if you do a run, I do the sponsorship. That's a good bet. Now off you go, we're done here."

I wandered out of the surgery, back to my car, thinking what sort of run does he mean? Must be some local fun run or something, but even so, I can't run with the *overhang*, so it's completely irrelevant. The bottom line was that I didn't want to do a run, and he doesn't want to pay for it I thought, so I decided to ignore it, and hope it would go away. Anyway it was time to get back into town to work. Once I'd parked the car I decided to bring forward my coffee break, so popped round the corner to pick up my Daily Telegraph and into my local Italian café for a cappuccino. As I stirred in my sweeteners, there, sitting innocently on the front page, trying to pretend to mind its own business is an advert. Well, a promotional thing about registering online for a Daily Telegraph readers' ballot. I usually pass these things by without a second thought, but something drew my eye onwards. This ballot was for the first 2000 places in the Great North Run 2007.

It's a conspiracy! Clearly the forces of fate have ganged up and hatched a foul and dastardly plot to get me. Hey ho – que sera, sera!

The mind immediately started to wander – it was Doris Day, wasn't it, who sang that?

One quick crossword later, (the Cryptic is still undefeated by my sad little efforts) and I'm back at my desk entering the online ballot with the confidence that goes hand-in-hand with the knowledge that if it's really a conspiracy led by fate then it is certain I will get a place. Once they confirm, I'll find out what it's all about, how long it is, when it takes place and all that good stuff. Some days later an email pops up explaining that I have been unlucky in the Daily Telegraph pre-ballot, but they have forwarded my name, along with all other unsuccessful names, into the main ballot. I had absolutely no idea whatsoever how these things worked, but assumed fate would get me a place from the main ballot. There was no need to worry.

Time passed by, and somehow I managed to just keep doing the same stuff at the gym. There was no need to worry about this running stuff yet, not until I knew what was really going on. It's a strange sort of mental limbo, two mutually opposite thought processes cancelling each other out. On the one hand a total acceptance that fate has decided I will do this Great North Run thing, which on reflection I think I might have seen on the TV on occasion. On the other hand, it is a complete denial of any need to start preparation, as I haven't actually got an entry yet. Not only that, but here we are in late February, and this run thing isn't until the end of September anyhow.

Finally the ballot takes place, and the email comes through telling me that I haven't got a place.

What do you mean – I haven't got a place? It's FATE. I am SUPPOSED to be given a place!

This can't be happening; this is NOT what was ordained. Don't these people understand?

Eventually I read on through the email, to discover that 'you can still participate in the Great North Run 2007'. All I have to do is look at the list of charities that have places, and contact them to ask to run on their behalf. Now this makes sense, especially as the *bet* with Dr Ken was for me to do a run, and him to sponsor me for charity. At this point, I realise that I don't actually have, nor ever have had, a charity in mind. Yes, of course I've made donations to charities over the years, sponsored people doing things, bought flags, and worn my poppy with pride, but this is different. This is going to be serious fundraising, probably.

So I start to look through the list of worthy causes to see if any of them strike any sort of chord. I had no idea at all of the charities that got themselves involved in this sort of thing, and certainly not the foggiest that this was actually a really immense source of revenue for them. All the usual *suspects* were there, from Cancer and Kidney Research through to Oxfam, Guide Dogs, RNLI and of course I mustn't forget err...Alzheimer's (sorry...couldn't resist it!).

But then one popped up and hit me between the eyes – The Prostate Cancer Charity. Never heard of them before, but I didn't need to look any further. By way of an explanation, over the past few years I had witnessed the deaths of a number of close acquaintances to prostate cancer. In fact one of my very good friends from the Fuengirola Residents Association, The Poseur (who had acquired his nickname from a very occasional habit of sporting particularly *designer* bits and pieces on our trips), was at this very moment undergoing treatment for it, having been diagnosed the previous autumn. I immediately went to have a look at their website, and was taken aback by the extent of their work, and the services they offered both to sufferers and to the field of research into potential cures. This was truly the charity for me; the cause I would be prepared to support on behalf of so many people I knew and cared about.

I called them up, they emailed me the paperwork, and in next to no time I had a confirmed place to run in The Great North Run 2007, together with a guarantee to raise at least £400 in return for the entry. That's that then, I thought. I AM going to do a run.

At this point it also occurred to me that I should find out a little about this run. Just what had I committed myself to? I started to check through the Run's website for information, and very quickly realised that it was a HALF MARATHON.

"Oh shit!!"

THIRTEEN POINT ONE MILES OF RUNNING.

I'm certain that this was NOT what the doctor had ordered. He had meant a nice little 5k run, something like the 'Race for Life', and here I had gone blundering thoughtlessly into the pure nightmare of a HALF MARATHON. Several deep breaths later, I had begun to realise that actually, with six months to get used to the idea, this was going to be a great way to *do a run*. I bet myself that Dr Ken would be amazed at the idea, as would virtually everyone I knew, and that this could actually turn out to be a bit of laugh.

So when I arrived at the gym that same night I calmly informed Masochistic Mickey that I was going to do the Great North Run and that my place is confirmed.

"But you don't do running, Mike." is his response.

"I do now." I retort.

When is it, where is it, how long is it – the questions just flowed out. On 30th September, Newcastle, half marathon come the rehearsed replies.

"If you had told me that six months ago, I'd have fallen over laughing", says Mickey, "but I know better with you now. Let's sort out a programme."

It's March, so we cobble together a simple plan for the six months to the race, and I head off to the treadmill to see what this running lark feels like. Meanwhile another of the gym staff, Ben, who has a little running experience, comes over to advise me to go to a local running shop of whose existence I had previously been blissfully unaware, to get myself some proper running shoes. I explain that I recently acquired some nice trainers, but he is totally insistent, and backed up by Mickey, so I make a mental note to do as I'm told.

Normally on the treadmill I power walk with a high incline setting as a good cardiovascular workout, but tonight Mickey advises me to drop the incline to a very low level, and increase the speed to a jog. Immediately the main problem manifests itself in a quite painful way. This is clearly not going to work without some serious intervention.

I now explain the problem with a simple description delivered with a smile,

"It is the gentleman's version of the *Dolly Parton effect*, if you get my meaning!"

In the old seaside postcard joke, the extremely *well-endowed* lady tries jogging and ends up with two black eyes. In my case, the extremely large *overhang* of, by now useless, excess skin immediately flops up and down as soon as I try to start jogging, creating a catastrophically painful collision with my testicles on every descent. This is clearly not going to work without some method of holding it firmly in place. I turned down the speed to a walk again, and left running to another day.

The next email to arrive is from The Great North Run people, confirming my place, and offering all sorts of good advice for the novice runner. I am now well into *soak up and use all information* mode, but one particular tip leaves me wondering – *Start a training blog on Realbuzz.* Now I'd heard of these *blogs*, but had never ventured to actually look at any. They were some sort of diary, weren't they, that anyone could look at on the internet. So I went onto the realbuzz.com website, and spent a while looking at some of the blogs in the *great runs* section. It seemed that there were a lot of people doing these things, and any time they asked for advice or help, there were always replies from other blog people to help out or answer the questions. Maybe, just maybe, this warranted some thought. I went back for another look, and started to pick up on the types of nicknames people used, the fact that they had *overviews* as a sort of simple introduction to themselves, and *profiles* to characterise themselves for anyone interested. If I was going to do as instructed and take yet another plunge into the unknown, I would clearly have to decide on my profile, my nickname, and what on earth to write about myself.

Dr Ken's "I think you should do a run" was starting to snowball, and clearly it was turning into a whole new project with boundaries that were expanding all the time.

In the end, I finally decided to take the plunge. But first I would have to decide on a nickname to blog under – my *blogname*. Then my mind shot back to that FRA Christmas lunch up in Edinburgh, and Para Handy's decision that I should now be known as The Incredible Shrinking Man. Perfect! So *The Incredible Shrinking Man* blog was created, and the sign off TISM was used for the very first time.

MY FIRST BLOG'S OVERVIEW

Hi, my friends have started to call me The Incredible Shrinking Man, because, over the last two years, I have managed to reduce myself from 27.5 stone to 13.5 stone (I am officially less than half the man I was). I had never set foot inside a gym, but have used my local Bannatyne's for the last 10 months, and much to my surprise I actually enjoy it.

Now, at 53, and never having done a run before, I am going to do the Great

North Run for Prostate Cancer. This is a direct result of my new philosophy of trying never to say No to something I haven't tried before. Life is way too short for missed opportunities.

In case anyone wonders, I have not used any of the diet plans – my secret is a completely new found willpower – (there are no reasons not to – only excuses).

I have never attempted a blog of any kind, but as there were no reasons not to – here I go...!! I have no idea what this going to turn into, but the only way to find out is to do it. All comments will be most welcome – I have the feeling that I am going to need all the encouragement I can get.

This project was rapidly taking on a life of its own, but I still hadn't even run a step, got running shoes, or started a training plan. It was high time I got serious about this and found out if I could actually do it at all, before things went any further. So I went shopping, something which I normally avoid like the plague. I will never ever understand the concept of Retail Therapy, clearly a feminine speciality beyond my simple thought processes. As far I was concerned, the only time these two words deserved to be in close proximity to each other was when explaining that I needed therapy after a retail experience. Nevertheless, I girded my loins, metaphorically speaking, and hit the city centre on a mission to find something in one of the sports shops to *hold everything in place* for running. Eventually, after hours of browsing, trying on and rejecting just about everything that might have worked, I finally found exactly what I was looking for. They were black, some sort of neoprene, rather like a cut down version of a diver's wet suit. About 5mm thick and encasing everything from my waist to my knees without compromise. Technically, they were called *compression shorts*! Without this find, I would most certainly not have been able to run, so I can forgive them anything. But on a long hot summer run, they took on the characteristics of a blast furnace, and eventual removal was always accompanied by a small steam cloud forming in the locker room at the gym. So I cleared out the small supply they had, added a couple of likely looking running vests, and went on my way rejoicing.

Next was the trip to Advance Performance – the *running shop* on an out-of-town retail & industrial park. This was a complete eye opener in so many ways, and brought to an abrupt close the days of buying trainers because they looked good, and seemed comfortable sitting in the shop. The simple opening remark:

"I need to buy some running shoes" was the trigger for a re-enactment of the Spanish Inquisition.

"What sort of running?"

Oh come on, I thought, how many types of running are there?

"The one foot in front of the other quicker than usual, sort of running!"

"Road, off-road, trail, sprinting, track running, long distance running?"

"Err...I am going to do the Great North Run in September."

"Great. What running do you do at the moment? Have you brought your current running shoes with you?"

"I don't do any running at the moment, and so I don't have any current running shoes."

Then it was a sit down in the corner, and a few questions about injuries at any stage of life, followed by a check of the shoes I was wearing, and my foot measurements. All these were noted down on a card, accompanied by name, address and anything else that sprung to their mind.

Finally, a pair of running shoes was brought out for me to try on and check the fit. These seemed perfectly good to me; they fitted well, and didn't look too bad, so I asked how much they were.

"You probably won't want these. They are just for an initial assessment."

Now they had lost me completely.

Dave, the running shoe man, (it had seemed appropriate to be introduced if we were going to spend some together, as I now suspected) explained the process we would go through to find the right shoe. It involved running on a treadmill in the shop, with my feet being recorded on video. Then looking at the playback in slow motion to see how my feet performed throughout a contact with the road. This would be followed by trying a different carefully selected shoe, until we eventually saw a picture where my feet were touching down, rolling forward, and leaving the ground, with my Achilles tendon, up the back of my ankle, remaining close to vertical throughout. I had no idea that the trainers you see on an ordinary sports shop display are so carefully designed to make your feet work correctly, and that without this knowledge, the chances of getting a trainer which is precisely wrong for your foot, as opposed to precisely right, remain startlingly high. Some make your foot roll outwards and some inwards. The aim is to make your foot work so that the Achilles tendon in the back of the ankle remains precisely vertical throughout the running *gait*.

Finally, once the correct type of support had been identified on the treadmill video, a choice of three shoes was offered, all of which did the same support thing. Now I was expected to try each pair on, and go for a run around the car park outside the shop until I was sure which pair felt the most comfortable to run in. I eventually settled on a pair of Brooks Glycerin 5s, and about an hour or so after dropping in, I made my exit with my shiny new running shoes. By now I have come to love this process, and, of course, to know it by its real name – a gait analysis. (Dave, in the meantime, has become a friend, and my *running shoe guru.*)

I'm now on a roll! I've got a race entry, a training blog, my compression shorts, some white socks and fancy running vests, my running shoes, and a *masterplan* from Masochistic Mickey.

Do I need anything else? I asked myself.

Yes, came the response, *You need to do some running*!

CHAPTER TEN

DO I KNOW YOU?

DURING THAT FEBRUARY AND MARCH, WHILE THE WHOLE QUESTION OF *doing a run* was becoming an entry to the Great North Run, the *B Plan* course was continuing apace. I had to come to terms with strange things, like the fact that FAT is an essential part of a healthy diet. Not going to get technical here, but unsaturated fat is more or less good, saturated fat is more or less bad, but the hydrogenated stuff is the real killer. The food manufacturers make hydrogenated fats by blasting liquid oils with hydrogen to turn them into solid fats to provide longer shelf lives for baked products and give a more *satisfying* sensation in the mouth.

These things cause no end of nastiness to cell function, and cholesterol levels, so we were shown some food labels to help us identify them. We also looked at the energy density of foods, which is the basic calorie to weight ratio, and the amazing range of numbers calories in different manufacturers versions of what you would otherwise assume were exactly the same products. Our homework that week was to go around the shops we used, and actually read the food labels to see the distribution of these fats in some of our normal shopping. This was a real eye-opener in many ways, but I was pretty happy to see that I had more or less come to the right conclusions on most things over the last year or two. The main *rule* I took from this first part of the course, and which I still use now, is a very simple one, and easy to spot very quickly on almost everything in supermarkets when shopping.

Maximum 150 kcals per 100 grams.

In week 4 of the course, at the end of February, we were hit with a halfway weight check, and I have to say that I was simply staggered by the fact that some of the people on the course had actually put on a pound or two. The second half of the course was not quite so interesting, and concentrated on a whole bunch of things which frankly ought to have been second nature to everyone there. I suppose for the younger folk it is a sad reflection that these things were not the automatic facts that were drummed into my generation. Fresh fruit is good for you and fresh vegetables simply cooked are better than processed. These are things we took for granted from an early age, but it appears that for many nowadays the prospect of cooking vegetables from raw can be quite daunting. The final message of the course was fairly straightforward, and has long been another of my mantras, one that I pass on to anyone and everyone that ever mentions wanting to lose weight. At times I even embellish it a little – in an attempt to give it a little more *impact* on the unwary.

If you put in more fuel than you burn, then you put on weight.
If you put in the exact fuel that you burn, your weight stays steady.
If you put in less fuel than you burn, you lose weight.

Now I know that it is a little more complicated than that, but as a basic principle it is perfect. The beauty is that you have a free choice of changing any element whenever you want, as long as the equation remains the same. If you can't reduce fuel input, then increase the burn, or accelerate downwards, like I had been doing, by both reducing fuel input AND increasing the burn. The embellishment, for those struggling to grasp the concept, is that:

The only people I can think of who are fed *involuntarily* are coma patients, and prisoners on hunger strike. Just about everyone else uses their own hands to put all their food into their mouth, and no one forces them.

The final act of the course was to check everyone and see who had hit their targets. Now mine had been to lose ½ stone in weight, and 3.5% of body fat, and I managed to lose 1 stone 1 lb, and lose 4% of body fat, so I marked that down as a very distinct success. More important to me, however, was the fact that at the end of the course they calculated my BMI as 27.3, which meant I was now extremely close to my target of 27. This would be the trigger for the surgical team to whip into action, not that the people on the course knew anything about that. I wasn't going to talk about that publicly until I knew it was a definite fact, and I've known the National Health Service for long enough not to count any chickens in their farmyard.

Meanwhile my gym programme had been progressing well during the winter, but it was approaching time for one of the regular reviews. It is more or less essential to change your routine in the gym every two or three months, or you get into a rut. It is simply not possible to work on all muscle groups in a gym programme, so you have to rotate around to keep a balance or you end up over developing some areas and neglecting others. It also helps to prevent you getting bored with the same old routine for months on end. Now this review happened to coincide with my telling Masochistic Mickey that I was going to do the Great North Run, and once he had got over the shock he went to work on a specific schedule that would get me there in Newcastle, at the end of September, more or less ready to do the thing. I knew nothing about running or training for running, let alone running half marathons, so I was content in the knowledge that the guys at the gym were experts in this sort of thing, so I would do whatever they told me to do. To be utterly fair to them, I followed their programme, and all was well, but in retrospect they were definitely not running coaches, and no one should think that anything that follows in this section is a really good way to train for running such distances. It will certainly work for a one-off attempt, but proper, well balanced running training it is certainly not. But for now, ignorance was bliss, and I got down to it with gusto.

The new programme was absolute simplicity. We were at mid-March, and the Great North Run was at the end of September, so on the first week I had to get to 3 miles, the following week 4 miles. Then in April I had to go up to 5 miles, May 6 miles, June 7, July 8, August 9, early September 10, and this would be enough to get me round the full 13.1 miles on the day. The idea was to do 2 runs per week, one in the gym on the treadmill on a Wednesday, and one outside somewhere on a Sunday, running both sessions at a fairly even pace. The idea was that as the runs outside increased in length they would build my mental endurance, as well as help on the physical stamina side which would be enhanced by some weights and CV sessions in the gym for toning and upper body strength.

So on the 19th March, kitted out with my wonderful *compression shorts*, I went for a run on the treadmill in the gym, and managed 3 miles without too much bother. Guess it goes to show that all the gym work I had been putting in had really had a pretty good effect on my fitness levels. I followed this up with a run outside, actually up the tarmac path beside the river and then up along the rowing lake and back, total 4 miles, on the 25th March. My running had finally started properly, and it felt a bit better than I had honestly expected. But after a 4 mile run, the thought of doing that run three times in a row without stopping, then adding on another mile and a bit for the fun of it, was perfectly daunting. What on earth had I been thinking? OK, it was way too late to back out, but for goodness sake, did people really do this for *fun*, for sport. Did they really join clubs and go out running together as a *hobby*?

As usual, I stuck to the plan, more or less, and racked up a total of 10 miles in March! *(Yes, that's right, I only did one more 3 mile run on the treadmill – but it sounds so much better as a total of 10 miles!)*

During the first week of April I did two runs outside; 4 miles and 4.5 miles. Then it was time to see my doctor again, and I had a few things to discuss this month. However, not surprisingly, he took the wind out of my sails again.

"The weight's OK at 13 stone" he said.

"What do you mean, OK? That means I've lost over 14 ½ stone, I'm less than HALF what I was when I started! That's not just OK! That's *bloody marvellous*!"

"Yes. I know. And if you carry on like this you'll be down to a BMI of 27 next month and we can send you back to the surgeon. Now how's the running?"

Always grounded was Dr Ken, my rock through all of this. But then he got me worried when he took my blood pressure and pulse, and announced that he was going to have to send me for tests.

"Whoa there. What tests?"

"I have to send you for an ECG, check your heart properly. It's the rule when I record a heart rate like I just got on that check."

This had me worried now, however much he reassured me that this was standard procedure. We'd been doing this for a couple of years now, and he'd never *sent me* for tests before. And HEART tests as well

– never a good sign in your fifties. He explained at great length that the exercise and weight loss had improved my heart strength enormously, and that I now had a really strong, but very slow heart rate, normally seen in the likes of top athletes. But the rules meant that anytime anyone was seen with a heart rate that low, they had to cover themselves by getting a full ECG to make absolutely certain. He was sure that there would be no problem, but he couldn't write that number down in my notes without sending me for the check-up. So the following Monday I went for my ECG, wires were attached everywhere and then I was hooked up to the machine which duly whirred away for a while and spouted reams of paper. The lady operator had a long look at the traces, then another long look, and refused to tell me anything as it was up to the doctor to read them and tell me. Huge relief all round when he pronounced that everything was in better than perfect working order and that I had no right really to have a heart trace that good. End of worries (there was never a dull moment though, when I got together with Dr Ken!).

Not long after this little episode I stumbled across another new phenomenon one night at the gym. I had finished my workout upstairs in the main gym, and had gone down for my usual little session in the steam room and Jacuzzi as a reward for a good workout. I was doing a couple of lengths of the pool before popping into the steam room when I noticed that an old friend from the Rotary Club was swimming. I hadn't seen him there before, didn't even know he was a member, so was quite surprised to see him. In fact I probably hadn't seen him at all for probably 18 months or more. It was Tony, the guy who organised the annual 10k road race for the club, and who had been something of a runner in the past himself.

"Hi Tony." says I, all innocently. He ignored me. "Hi Tony", says I, slightly more insistently.

"I'm sorry. I didn't realise you were talking to me. Do I know you?"

Now this is a guy I had dinner with every week for years. He had a very good little printing works, and had done all my business printing for a couple of companies that I had been running for a while. And here he was, claiming not to know who on earth I was? When I explained, in words of one syllable who I was, he initially refused to believe me, but eventually realised that he did, in fact, recognise my voice, if not the body it came from!

This was the first time, apart from the fun with the guys in Scotland, that I had really encountered the simple fact that I was now unrecognisable even to my local old friends and acquaintances, and it took a bit of getting used to. We eventually ended up in the coffee bar for a longer chat, and I was able to tell him that I was actually training to do The Great North Run. This again took him a few minutes to assimilate, as he had certainly never envisaged having to think of me doing a run like that. But he was quick off the mark, and in no time at all had persuaded me to run in the Deepings 10k race on 20th May, as,

"It would be at the perfect point in your training, for the half marathon, and you will need to have some race experience."

Eventually I agreed, but only after he had spiced it up with a slightly naughty little scheme. He would slip my entry through the computer system, which he controlled anyway, without telling anyone at the Rotary Club. On the day of the race I should just turn up, line up, and go, and we could safely assume that no one else would recognise me. Then, during the race, he would casually tell all the rest of the guys so that they would know by the time I finished and could look out for me crossing the finish line. He would give me an easy to spot number, to help them all pick me out – in the end I had the running number 700. This definitely sounded like a bit of fun, and I was suckered into entering my first ever race!

It was about this time that I got an email from *Para Handy* telling me to look at a strange website that he had found. He wanted me to go on to it, and put in my stats from before I started losing weight and also my new stats now. Intrigued, I looked up the grim sounding link www.deathclock.com and found *The Death Clock* a weird website where you enter some simple facts about yourself, like body mass index and age, and it supposedly gives you your expected date of death. I was hooked immediately, so I began by putting in my *before* details, and then my new ones. The stark truth was that whilst previously it reckoned that I would have fallen very short of picking up my pension indeed, the *new me* apparently would last TWENTY FIVE YEARS LONGER! I know perfectly well that this site is probably based on life expectancy statistics used by the insurance companies, and that it is really just a bit of fun, but there is a strong element of truth behind it in an *all things considered* kind of way.

I now encourage anyone who is looking for extra motivation on their own weight loss journey to have a look. I usually advise them to put in their target weight and see the difference it will make. The potential outcome has a wonderful way of concentrating the mind, but it is not one for the superstitious or faint hearted.

By now I had also got used to posting entries on my blog on Realbuzz, and had quickly realised that there was a very interactive community of bloggers there. Any time you had any questions about any aspect of running, there were always plenty of folk willing and able to come up with all the right answers. I have always been the sort of guy who likes to understand as much as possible about anything I get myself into, so I was soaking up information like a sponge all the time. It was also apparent that my somewhat unusual background to running, through the weight loss and my slightly irreverent sense of humour, meant that I was getting a number of regular visitors and comments on my blog, and was getting to know a good number of people on the site. It was an easy habit to get into, posting a blog entry and checking to see what other regulars had been getting up to on most evenings. This *community spirit* side of the site became obvious when I mentioned that I was going to do this race, and immediately one of the other bloggers from fairly nearby signed up to do the race with me. At the same time, a number of the others were entering a 10k race to be held in June – the City of Manchester 10k, based at the new City of Manchester Stadium. Now Number One lives in Manchester, and I hadn't been over there for a while, so I decided to enter that race as well, as it would give me an excuse to see her, and also to meet finally with a number of people that I was *talking* to on an almost daily basis. So I entered online, and then stepped back and realised that I was no longer just *doing a run*, but I was now actually entered in three races! Only problem was that I still hadn't run any further than 4½ miles yet, and I was now supposed to do two races of 6.2 miles in a few weeks. Had I lost some marbles, somewhere along the way, without realising?

Actually, alongside entering races, my right knee had been hurting a little at the end of that second run in the first week of April, and while

I was unsure of what caused it I didn't want to aggravate anything, so cut back for a while to just doing my normal gym programme. I didn't run at all the second week, but finally had a run on the treadmill in the third week to see if everything was still in working order. I was pleased that there was no recurrence of any discomfort, and managed a steady 3 miles without any problems. This was followed by a couple more runs over the next few days, and then as the end of the month loomed it dawned on me that the Deepings race was only three weeks away. The race was 10k, or 6.2 miles, and the furthest I had run was 4.5 miles, and that was the run when my knee felt funny. It was time to at least make a serious attempt at running the race distance, or I could be making a real fool of myself on the day. Looking back I have no idea how I managed to do such a distance on a treadmill, but that is indeed what I did. In fact I ran 7.4 miles on that infernal machine, and now knew for certain that I could at least run the race distance with a bit to spare in the tank. It was not very fast, and it was not very pretty, but it was at least done now! April's total became 25 miles – quite a step up from March.

During the first couple of weeks of May I managed to get a run in every other day, ranging from 2 to 7 miles, some in the gym on the treadmill, some outside along the river bank and out towards the lakes in the country park. The running, backed up with the more intensive gym programme, was clearly turning some of the remaining fat into muscles, in places where I had no real idea that I should have muscles. Now as muscle weighs more than fat, this was not the clearest way to a short term weight loss – but I reasoned that I was not after a short term weight loss programme, so as long as the toning I was getting was making sure I didn't have too much loose skin around the body showing up as *bingo wings* or a *floppy neck* then it was doing all I could ask for.

May's check with the doctor revealed a couple more pounds were gone, and he was now happy to refer me back to the reconstructive surgery team as I would probably have lost the last little bit by the time I got an appointment. When I got home I noted down my latest weight on the spreadsheet I had drawn up so that I could see how I was progressing, and something made me play around with some calculations. I had actually lost over 200 pounds, and I was more surprised than anyone else that I had actually been able to achieve that amazing number. Mind you, although I had worked hard enough to ensure that I did not have folds of loose skin in places where they would look unsightly to normal public scrutiny, I did have the most advanced huge flap of loose skin hanging down from my stomach, and the inside edges of my thighs were by now looking pretty grim too.

I went for one more run on the Wednesday before the race, and before I knew it I was all kitted out in my running gear, parked up, and walking into the Deeping Rugby Club which they used as Race Headquarters each year. This was going to be the real test, in more ways than one! First and foremost, it would be a test of how on earth I would get on in an actual running race. Me, in a running race, voluntarily, for goodness sake, who would ever have thought it? Secondly, it would be a test of whether any of the guys would actually recognise me, which would just be a bit of fun. Thirdly, it would be a test of how they reacted when they found out, and in a weird way this was actually extremely important to me, as it would be a really good indication of how almost anyone I had known over the years would probably react. I had to find out, and not least I had to see how I reacted to their reaction, it was a sort of defining moment hiding behind playing a fun trick on some good guys.

As I walked into the club house I could see that two of the club stalwarts were manning the late registrations desk, Mike and Derek. I knew perfectly well that I had no reason to speak to them as I was long since registered, and had my number pinned on my vest already, but I couldn't resist the chance.

"Excuse me Gents, I've already got my number and stuff, but do I have to sign in or anything?"

"No. You're fine. We don't need to check you in."

Hurdle one cleared with ease, absolutely no recognition in the slightest. Now to be fair to the guys, I was dressed in running gear, and on reflection I was brushing my hair slightly differently, but no recognition in the slightest! Not even a second glance. At that point I spotted Tony doing his race director thing in the corner, and wandered over and said "Hi" in passing. He smiled broadly, and quietly said that he would tell them all as soon as all the runners had left the field on the race.

Heading back outside I passed any number of the guys getting set up for their various roles, and managed to offer a "Hi" or a "Good

Morning" to every one of them I spotted, and all with the same result – that is no result. At this point I met up with Mel, a blogger from the Realbuzz site who was also training for the Great North Run and had decided to come and run this race when she had read about it on my blog. Number Three and her boyfriend also showed up at this point. None of the others were able to get there for the race, so she was on *Keep an eye on Dad and phone to tell us which hospital they've taken him to duty* for the others. All of a sudden it was approaching race time, so I did my last few warm up stretches, and walked across to the far side of the field with all the other runners ready to line up. By now I was taking note of what the other 200 or so runners looked like, and it was clear that there were some pretty serious runners around, and very large contingents from what were clearly local running clubs judging by their various running colours. Actually the best clues were the names of the running clubs on the vests in big letters, but please cut me some slack; it was my first time taking note of such things! At this point discretion was very clearly called for, so trying to look cool and as if this was a normal Sunday morning pursuit, I slipped towards the back of the line up so as not to get in anyone's way. At this point I also said "Good Luck" to Mel, who was looking like a Whippet straining at the leash, and it was clearly the last time I would see her before the end of the race, and only then if she hung around to wait for me. Tony then took out his megaphone and gave everyone their last instructions, and the countdown began.

CHAPTER ELEVEN

OLD FRIENDS & A NEW FACE

NEXT THING I HEARD A HOOTER BEING SOUNDED, AND THE RACE HAD started. Up at the front of the pack, they took off like greased lightning, but I quickly realised that that there were a good few more at home at the back, and intent on keeping to a much more civilised and sedate pace, so I wasn't going to be running alone. The route began by taking us through the edges of the main residential area for about a mile or so, where there were a good few folk around clapping and encouraging the runners. At each junction there was a yellow-bibbed marshal making sure that everyone was OK and going in the right direction, and I recognised practically all of them from the Rotary Club. The runners around me have by now thinned out a good deal, so I was able to call out a greeting to each Marshall by name, as I passed. In every case there was a mild query obvious on their face, as they failed to recognise someone who clearly knew them by name, and it took my mind off the running for short stretches.

Soon we cleared the housing area, and were now out on some back lanes for the rest of the course. This was real *fenland*, flat as a pancake for as far as the eye can see, and I remembered to thank the gods that they had seen fit to keep the weather fine and calm. This could clearly be a pretty evil course if the weather was to turn nasty, as there was no shelter of any kind whatsoever. The runners were really thinning out now, but I could see the whole of the rest of the route across the fields, and it wasn't so funny to see just how far ahead the leading runners already were.

A couple of miles into the race, was the water station, strategically positioned so that it served both directions at just the right stages of the race. Some of the *usual suspects* were serving up plastic cups of water to the runners, so it was another chance for some confusing name-dropping. Mind you, trying to drink cold water from a plastic cup whilst running is virtually guaranteed to bring you to a choking halt, so discretion dictates a walk break to make sure the drink goes down safely in the right direction. A little further on and the route went off on a very long loop of a couple of miles, before coming back on itself and returning along the same route back to the rugby club. I was relieved to get to the loop before any of the leaders were coming the other way, saving a small degree of potential embarrassment, and at the turn I spotted Tony's son acting as marshal there. He was the only other co-conspirator, and was kind enough to give me some really heartfelt encouragement to keep me heading on.

After playing cat and mouse with some of the other back-markers for a couple of miles, most of whom, like me, had by now resorted to what is known as a *run-walk* strategy (run 5 or 10 minutes, walk one minute) I finally turn onto the last long straight lane towards the finish, but by now I'm feeling seriously knackered and just about ready to walk the last 1,000 yards. At this point, Tom, another friend I'd known for years, and who had done a fair bit of jogging in his time, appeared alongside me on his bike. I remembered that I had mentioned to him a couple of weeks back that I would be doing the race, and he had come out looking for me especially to support me on the run. He kept me going, chatting away, all down that long stretch, and really helped me a lot just when I needed it.

Finally I reached the turn into the rugby field, and the final couple of hundred yards across the grass to the finish line. What a wonderful sight a finish line makes at the end of a race, I had clearly never appreciated the finer points of their beauty before. Crossing that line was accompanied by a smattering of cheers from the few supporters still waiting around, the majority having found their way by now into the bar of the rugby club for something to eat and a hot drink. My daughter was clearly hugely relieved to see me back safe and well and with a smile on my face, and the looks of astonishment on the faces of the finish line officials, who had by now been told to look out for me finishing, was a picture.

Officially I had now finished my first race, the Deepings 10k, in a time of 66 minutes 38 seconds, and was placed 189th out of 201 finishers, so wasn't last either. Not bad from only 2 months of running training, in my mid fifties, to go out on a Sunday morning and do a race just over 6 miles long.

Once I had got myself a couple of cups of water, and collected my finishers' commemorative mug, we headed for the bar as well to get warmed up and also to have some proper conversations now with the Rotary Club guys who had all been told by Tony, but were reluctant to believe it. Probably needless to say, they were completely astonished! Not only did they have the complete shock of seeing my *new and improved shape*, which they found extremely hard to believe, but they also had to get used to the fact that I had just run their 10k race, probably the last person on the planet that they would ever have believed would run it. Congratulations flew thick and fast, and I certainly didn't have to pay for any of the food the ladies were serving up, or any drinks. The biggest question of the day was clearly:

"How?"

How had I managed to lose the weight; how had I not got wrinkles of loose skin on my face, my neck, my arms etc. I was still in my running vest, so it was perfectly plain that I had managed to get reasonably well toned given the amount of weight lost, and to be honest, it was probably the best sort of clothes to be wearing as they could really see the new me (if still just a little bit on the sweaty side).

While I was thoroughly enjoying the attention and praise, Tony came over and told me that he wanted to have a chat properly, but that he had to sort out the final results and arrange for the prize presentations so that the winners could collect their spoils and get off home. So he asked if I'd mind hanging on and he would see me and buy me a drink as soon as they got it over and done with. I was in no rush to go anywhere, so I told him it would be fine, and I would hang on. Mel and her boyfriend, and Number Three and her boyfriend had Sunday lunches to go to, so they said their farewells and left, and I stayed on chatting while we waited for the presentations. To be honest, I'd never been to anything like this before, even when I had helped out a few years before. I had always done my bit and then disappeared rather than hang around with a load of fit people. So I was quite interested to see who the best runners were, and which running clubs they came from. It was not too long before they had sorted out the results, and had set up a table with a large number of plaques for the winning males and females, the age group winners, the winning male and female teams and I don't know what else.

Tony opened the proceedings with the Club President ready to start giving out the prizes. At this point I finally realised just how stitched up I had been, as his first announcement was about me doing the race. He explained to everyone about my weight loss, that this was my first ever race and they had a special plaque ready to give to me, amidst much flashing of camera bulbs and applause. This was so totally unexpected it took me quite unawares, and I was really struck by the warmth of the reaction from the other runners. Luckily I didn't have to say anything, but this gesture from the Club meant a huge amount to me. I had started the day wondering about how people would react, how they would look at me now, wondering if it would change any attitudes. The answer was very clear and bold now, and positive in every way. I had nothing to fear in the slightest, if anything I could even possibly detect a hint of respect for my achievement, and it was certainly making me feel good about myself in every way. The icing on the cake was that they told me that I couldn't have the plaque to keep yet, as they were going to have it engraved with my name and my time for the race – a fantastic gesture, and what a wonderful souvenir of my first ever race.

I finally managed to extricate myself and head out, as I was still in my running gear and was starting to become both unsightly and not a little malodorous – I needed a shower! I had realised that my trip home would take me past my gym club, so I had come prepared to stop off there for a shower, and also for a long slow session in the steam room and the Jacuzzi. I had certainly earned it, and it was a real treat after the morning's exertions. So much so, that I made a mental note to try to organise it so that I did this after any of my longer training runs. It also gave me the opportunity to have a comfortable lie down and reflect on the day. It had been so far out of the ordinary; I had enjoyed myself so much in many ways; I had been able to allay my fears about old friends' reactions to the *new me*, and I had taken the first proper step towards doing the Great North Run. It had been A GOOD DAY in every respect.

CHAPTER TWELVE

THE REALBUZZ GANG

MAY 2007, AS IF IT HADN'T QUITE FINISHED WITH ME YET, SERVED UP ONE last pleasant surprise before it left. I received a letter informing me that I had an appointment to see the consultant surgeon on 13th July. I was definitely impressed with their speed this time, not only the speed with which they had accepted the referral again and made an appointment, but that the date was so soon too.

I also made myself another appointment before the month was out. When I had got back to my car after the Deepings 10k there were a number of flyers popped under my windscreen wipers, and on every other car in the car park. Suspecting the usual load of rubbish about car boot sales and special offers at new hairdressing salons, I was surprised to find that they were all adverts for races organised by other local running clubs through the summer. To be honest, I had never realised that there was so much of this stuff going on around the area, and certainly I'd never realised the number of running clubs that appeared to be thriving right under my nose. Looking at the dates, distances and locations, I quickly worked out that most of them would not fit my schedule at all, but there was one 10k race, again quite close by, that looked good for the 1st July, the Thurlby 10k, so I popped off an entry without a second thought. I have no idea what on earth I was thinking about, as no other race was going to have the same fun and friendly atmosphere as that Rotary Club one, which was unique. I suppose in some way I was just thinking that a couple more shorter races would help me get properly prepared for the Great North Run, which was what it was all about. However, I did start to get concerned when it began to appear that I had made a serious miscalculation on this one.

Around the South Lincolnshire and North Cambridgeshire area is some of the flattest country ever fashioned by either God or nature, and I just made the natural assumption that as Thurlby was local, and I had driven past it a few times on the A15 and not noticed anything unusual, that it would naturally be another pretty flat course. Not long afterwards I bumped into Tom, the friend who had encouraged me to the finish at the Deeping 10k, and when I mentioned that I was also going to do the Thurlby 10k he looked surprised and asked:

"So you are going to take on Cardiac Hill are you?"

Whoops! This was not in the masterplan. It wasn't supposed to include running up anything that could possibly be described as *Cardiac Hill*. Homework was required immediately, and was obviously long overdue on this one! I took a drive out to Thurlby, with the course map downloaded from the internet, and introduced myself to Strawberry Hill, which took up a significant chunk of the first third of the course, winding its way up from the village to the site of the radio mast. From that day onwards I have (almost) never entered a race without checking the course profile in detail before even considering entering. It was a daunting prospect to someone of my limited running training, but it also made me go straight back to the Great North Run website and take a long hard look at the course profile there for the first time properly. It was not flat either, not by a long way. There are no really steep bits at all, but there are some long gentle inclines that go on and on, most famously (or should I say *infamously*) the notorious John Reid Road. My conclusion was that if, in fact, the Great North Run was not flat then it was probably a good idea to find out what running uphill was like sooner rather than later. Lesson learned.

June brought with it the realisation that I had to make sure that I was definitely below a body mass index of 27 by the time I saw the surgeon on the 13th July, as I didn't want any more delays, or excuses there. I had originally had no idea that surgery of this nature would be possible on the National Health Service, so had not really been expecting it at all. But once we had got this far with the surgical team, I could no longer envisage not having the surgery. To fail on some technicality now would be disastrous, as in the back of my mind I had already virtually had it. This gave a new edge and focus to the eating habits during June, although it would be fair to say that I didn't have to consciously make any efforts when cooking or shopping any more, it had become the normal routine to live by the new rules I had set myself. Not only could I actually walk past a burger bar in the street without giving it a second thought, but I even realised that I could buy something from one of these places for one of my girls if they wanted, and not buy something for myself.

I was sticking as well as ever to my gym and running training, but this extra exercise did need fuelling properly, so I began to look at the proper nutrition for the body to be able to do this much work. Not only was it new territory for my eating plans, it was a strange new world for my physical self as well, getting used to doing serious exercise and eating properly for it. As usual there was more information available than any one person could possibly read, and enough different plans and opposing ideas to try a different one every day of the year. It turned out that the low Glycaemic Index foods were perfectly suited to running as they released energy slowly. The only other main rule was to slightly increase the protein intake to help to maintain and repair muscles, so a little more meat and fish was added into the eating plan – particularly chicken and tuna as I especially like them, and I also allowed a little cheese back into the plan too (although the emphasis was on *a little* due to the fat content as well).

With the food side of things better organised for the amount of running I was now doing, I got on with the running! My simple little plan required me to be up to 7 miles in June, so I suppose typically, I ran 7 miles on the first of June. Now when I say I ran 7 miles, I don't want anyone to get the wrong impression here. This was not a full-blooded impression of an athlete, but more what I had by now realised was a thoroughly legitimate strategy referred to in distance running circles as a *run-walk* method. So it was very largely running, but with the odd *power walk* thrown in now and again to give my body a chance to keep up with my brain. The end result was an average pace of just over 11 minutes a mile, so a bit on the slow side, but totally satisfactory none the less. I followed this up with a 6 mile run on the 3rd, which felt really lousy, but recovered to do an 8 mile run on the 5th. I mixed in a couple of good gym sessions over the next week, and a couple of shorter runs taking advantage of the long evenings. The route I was using was along the side of the river, and into Ferry Meadows, our local country park about 2 miles away which had a tremendous selection of different paths around the lakes there, so it was always a pleasure to run in such peaceful and pleasant surroundings.

By now, I should have realised that this was all going far too smoothly. I was ahead of schedule on my training plan, and looking forward to the City of Manchester 10k on the 24th. I had booked a room in a hotel recommended by the running club organising the race, as Number One was working some pretty strange hours and I wanted to get a good night's sleep before the race. My brother and his family lived in Cheadle, on the southern edge of Manchester, and my mother lived a few hundred yards from them, but I wanted to keep away from them on this particular weekend. My nephew was getting married in September, and it was going to be a big family get-together. I had not actually seen any of them for a year or more, so apart from talking on the phone and mentioning I had *lost a bit of weight*, I had decided to maximise the impact just before the Great North Run, when the whole family would be together for the first time in ages. I was intending to wander into the hotel where we were all staying for the festivities, and basically see how long they took before they recognised me. I couldn't afford to spoil the surprise by dropping in on some of them now, so I made sure they had no idea I was going to be there that weekend. My nephew himself knew, as I had recently helped him to move. He was in the RAF, and was moving from RAF Brize Norton in Oxfordshire to RAF Marham in Norfolk, and hadn't passed his driving test yet, so I offered to do the honours as it was a lot easier for me, being near Marham, than for his Dad who was in Manchester. When I picked him and all his gear up, I had sworn him to secrecy – relatively easily bearing in mind his state of shock – and he had kept his word impeccably.

So all was set, and the trip to Manchester for my second race was fast approaching, when I went out for a run on the 15th June. I was cruising along comfortably about 6 miles into the run, when I suddenly got a sharp pain in my ankle, at the back around the Achilles tendon. I simply couldn't run on it any more, it was far too painful, and it hurt a fair bit just to walk on it. My only problem was getting home. How would I get home – I was out on deserted pathways on the edge of the park, with no money on me, not that that would have made any difference as I was a fair way away from the nearest road or bus route. I had no option but to walk the 2½ miles home on a dodgy ankle. It was not much fun, but I made it back OK. I remembered seeing a physiotherapist working at the gym, in fact I think he had his clinic set up in one of the rooms there, so I called the gym to get his number, and made an appointment to see him urgently. He quickly decided that it was Achilles Tendonitis – a strain in the tendon at the back of the ankle (in English). He hooked me up to various bits of equipment which apparently did strange and wonderful things (appropriate for people with Achilles Tendonitis), in the right places. Then he promptly announced that if I behaved myself, did as I was told, and came back to see him in a couple of days, that I would probably be all right in time for the race. Massive relief ensued, as I had feared the worst for a while there, and really didn't know what I would have done if he had told me I couldn't do the Great North Run after all.

At the end of that traumatic week, the Saturday was a theatre night. Number Four is a very talented actress and singer, and that's not just my highly biased opinion but the opinion of a number of local drama societies, and the main youth theatre group in the city. This group was putting on a performance of a clever piece of work called *Our Day Out* at the main theatre in the city. We all had an excellent evening's entertainment, and I got the excuse to spend a Saturday evening resting my ankle without having to explain it all to anyone.

The next week shot by in a blur of physiotherapy appointments, evenings in the steam room and Jacuzzi at the gym, rather than in the gym itself, and wondering whether I would be able to race at the weekend (or if my ankle would cope with driving all the way there first). Finally, on the Friday, Paul, the physio, told me that I would be fine to run on the Sunday, but to make sure that I rested the ankle till the race. This was a huge relief, as I had been looking forward to this race for weeks – well to be fair not necessarily looking forward to the race, but to meeting up with so many of the people I had *virtually* met on the blogging site, and who had been so supportive in their comments and encouragement.

So on the Saturday I drove the 160 odd miles over to Manchester, and booked into the hotel – once I had finally found it! Shortly after arriving I made contact with Number One on the phone, and she came over to the hotel. I don't know Manchester very well at all, so she drove us into the centre and we found a great little Italian restaurant for a delightful meal and a great catch-up chat. By now I had also come to know that pasta on the night before a race is almost obligatory for runners, as it gives you a high quality carbohydrate boost to increase your energy levels for the race. Although this is not so important for shorter races like the 10k that weekend, it is still a good idea. When preparing for longer races, like half marathons and full marathons, most training plans include what is known as *carb-loading* in the final few days before the run. This is to boost to the maximum energy stored by the body, which cannot normally store enough energy to fuel itself for a marathon. Running 26 miles will burn anything up to 4000 calories – which is more than the body can store (a bit like having a fuel tank in your car which will let you drive 400 miles, then trying to do 600 miles of driving), so *carb-loading* is like creating a short term auxiliary fuel tank for another 100 miles of driving. When the energy store runs out, that's when marathon runners *hit the wall* – they literally have the will to continue, but the body is no longer able to function as the muscles have no fuel left. So the more you boost the auxiliary energy tank the better – and on the run you need to take extra energy on board to fill that *gap* at the end, usually by taking special energy drinks.

Anyway, we went for a pasta meal even though it was only a 10k race – why tempt fate? We also both needed to head our separate ways quite early, she because of her work shifts, and me because I needed a good night's sleep ready for an early start in the morning. It was a real treat to spend an evening with her, as we didn't often get the chance for a one-to-one chat nowadays. But all good things must come to an end, so she dropped me back at the hotel, and I managed to avoid the lure of the bar and got my head down.

Race day saw me up bright and early for a quick breakfast, change into my running gear, and off in the car to try to find the race venue. It proved relatively simple, as it was at Sportcity, which included the City of Manchester Stadium – built for the 2002 Commonwealth Games and now home to the Manchester City football team, and the very much smaller athletics track. What really made it easy to spot was the quite remarkable giant sculpture, the tallest in Britain, known as the *B of the*

Bang which dominated the road junction on the corner of the site. I soon discovered that the name came from a quote by Linford Christie, the Olympic Sprinter, who said that he always started his races on the *B* of the Bang from the starting gun. Safely arrived, I parked in the enormous car park and joined the throng of runners and supporters making their way across to the athletics track where the race would start. This was a very different affair to the little run in the Deepings, as there were well over 1,000 runners participating, and the local radio station was covering the event live. I had numerous photographs of other bloggers burned into my memory, and it was remarkably easy to spot the first few, which led to all the others as they had already congregated together. The period up to the race itself was just a mad session of introductions, hugs, photos and excited chatter, broken only by quick toilet breaks and not so quick stretches and warm-ups as we prepared for the off. Leaving the various supporters and family members who had accompanied them in the stands, we all made our way to the track, wished each and everyone good luck, and merged into the crowd of runners. This was seriously different to anything I had ever attempted before, and was far from being a couple of hundred runners out on Sunday for a run round the village in aid of the local Rotary Club. I was not going to be singled out or given special plaques here, just merge into the background and hope that I didn't make too much of a fool of myself. Luckily, there was so much going on, and so many people talking to or at you, I clean forgot to worry about my dodgy ankle. I managed to insert myself about halfway back in the field of runners, and in a very short time the gun went and we were off.

The route was out of the athletics track, round the outside of the main stadium and the sculpture thing, then down the main road to the gasworks. Turn left and through the housing estate, ending back at the track, and on for a second lap. This lap was a bit shorter than the first, taking a different route through the local neighbourhood, and then the third and final lap was shorter still, missing the housing area and coming straight back through the car park, up the main approach to the big stadium, then veering off to finish on the athletics track. There was quite a large turnout of supporters at some parts of the course, and I was struck by how dramatically the route changed as you ran round. One moment you were running past a magnificent modern super-stadium, then past a world famous and very iconic sculpture, only to find yourself a few minutes later running through some pretty basic back streets scarred by a degree of clearly hard times. It appeared to me as if the organisers had found a way of showing us a microcosm of the extreme faces of the incredible mix which was the magnificent city of Manchester.

Eventually I approached the finish, and when I finally ran into the athletics track for the last couple of hundred metres it was a whole new experience to have a small crowd of bloggers cheering me home (needless to say I think they had all got back well before me, or at least the majority of them). The next, and surprising, new experience was to be ushered along after the finish, to keep out of the way of other runners finishing BEHIND me, and then to be handed a bag of goodies and a bottle of water by a pleasant young Army Cadet Corps lad. The pièce-de-résistance was being asked my size and handed a very smart race finishers T-shirt, before being politely moved on to the meet-and-greet area, where I was re-united with the Realbuzz Gang. Lots of photos were snapped at random, and cameras were handed around till there were no more angles, or groupings left to preserve for posterity. Performances were compared and contrasted, and I was struck by another simple but totally endearing reality about these running folk. No one cared at all if anyone had beaten them or were beaten by them, and race position comparisons were ignored. The only thing that mattered to every one of them was how they had done against their own record, and their own expectations. If someone had achieved a PB (Personal Best time for the distance) then that was a definite reason for celebration. In fact it *outranked* the performance of someone who might have run very much faster, but had been a bit slower than their usual time. On reflection, I realised that *technically* I had achieved a PB myself, as I had just clocked a time of 63 minutes and 44 seconds, a massive 2 minutes 54 seconds faster than my time at the Deepings 10k a month earlier, so that received much praise too. My position was 971 out of 1,114, so not last by quite a handsome margin.

In the end we all had to drag ourselves away as time progressed, and I had to get back to the hotel, grab a shower and a change into some proper clothes before check out time, which I actually managed. The drive back was pleasant and uneventful, which is in itself an event. It is almost unheard of for me to have a clear and unfettered run back across the Pennines, and down to the Fens. Normally the dreaded M62 and A1 conspire between them to create some sort of motoring chaos as soon as they realise I am in the vicinity, but they were in utterly benign mood that day, and provided me with another PB for the drive home. It had been a thoroughly successful and extremely enjoyable weekend in every respect, and it was already pretty clear that I had begun to gather a completely unexpected and delightful new circle of friends through this running and blogging routine. Looking back a year or two later, the folk I met at the City of Manchester 10k that weekend have remained good friends, constantly corresponding through the blogs, and meeting up randomly from time to time. Wendy, Russell, Paul, Martin, Laura, Andy and Jamie turned from being virtual people to real people, and from being virtual friends to real friends in the span of a single morning, and to a significant degree made another major contribution to what I had started to refer to mentally as *Project TISM*.

ABOVE
Mike, *second from right*, in the very early 1960s.

BELOW
Left to right: Mike in his early forties;
a little red wine is good for you, isn't it?;
playing around in the recording studio at Number
One's University, a year before the crash.

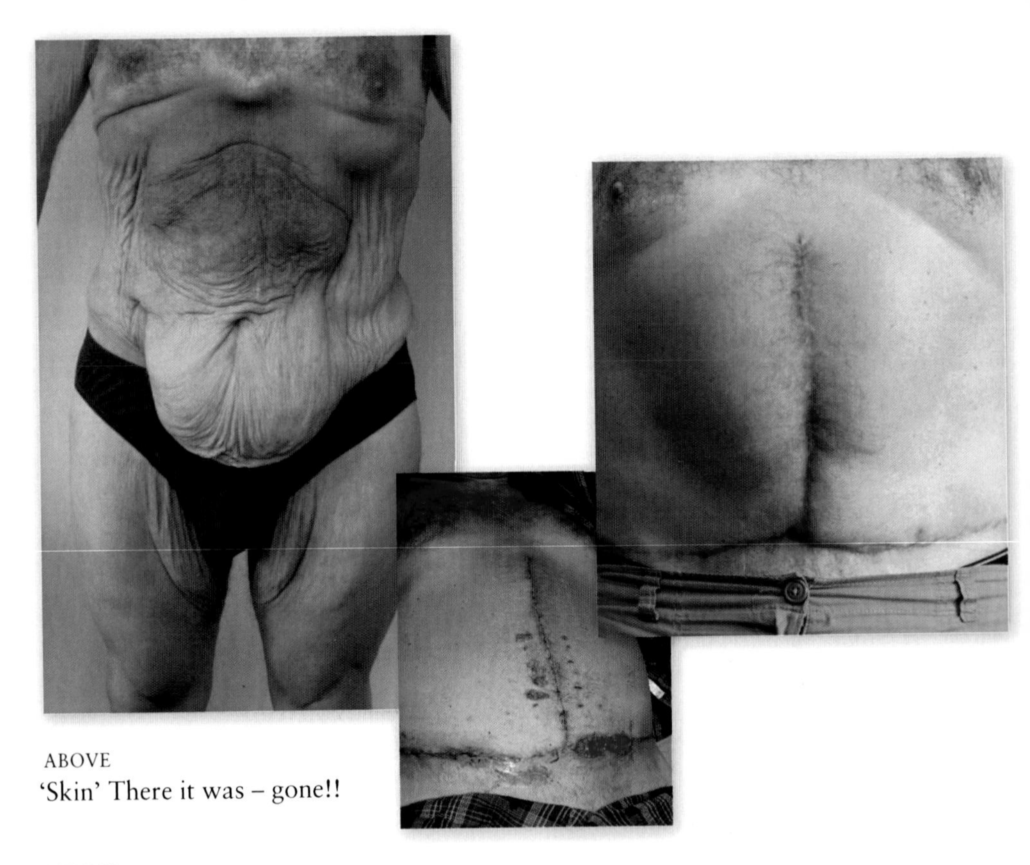

ABOVE
'Skin' There it was – gone!!

BELOW
Keeping it 'real'.

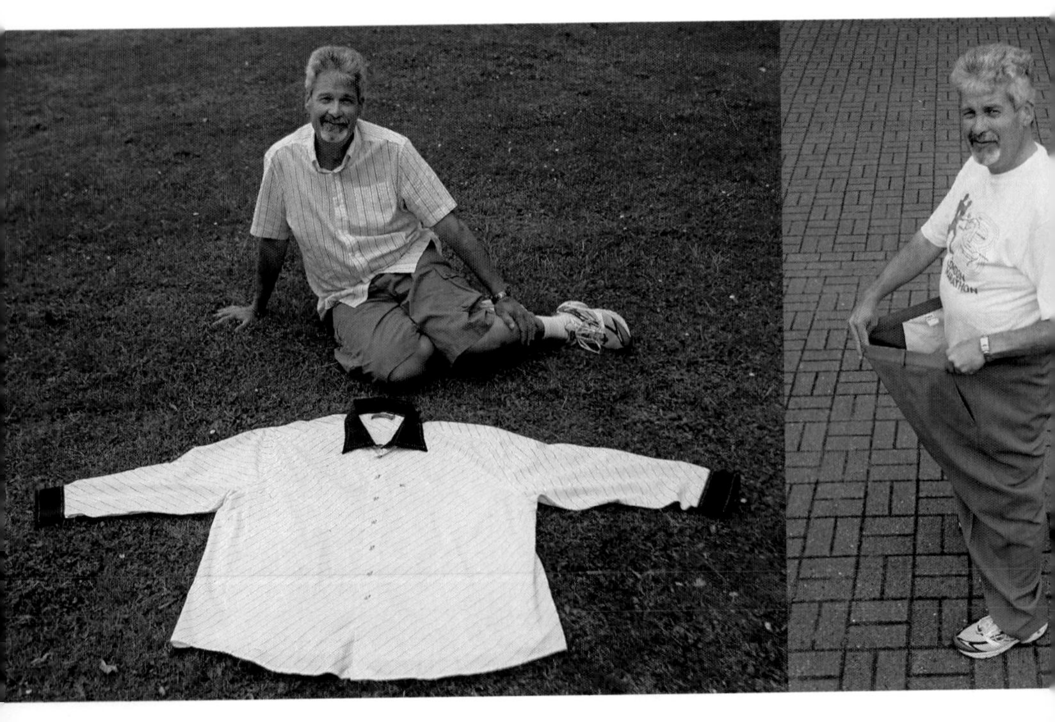

ABOVE
The President of The Rotary Club of the Deepings presents Mike with the plaque after his first race.

RIGHT
Mike in training for the London Marathon, Spring 2008.

-RAISER: Mike Hare, "the incredible shrinking man", at the finishing line of the Great North Run with his daughters. Inset, what he looked like in his bigger days.

he incredible shrinking an' runs with the stars

By MARK PEARSON

-RAISER got a surprise rt at the gruelling Great Run when he was invited live on the BBC before the

re, who is know as the incredi- ing man, lost a staggering 15 t three years, before deciding to ual race.

got to his Newcastle hotel race, he has a note to arrive at ly as he would be interviewed iple jump champion Jonathan

at Mr Hare was able to start at t of the race contingent. Lin- side celebrities such as Carol rower James Cracknell and ula Radcliffe.

aline coursing throu-

Daily Mirror WEDNESDAY 16.07.2008

FROM BLOB

..TO A BLOG

Web supporters help Mike shed 15st

AIDAN McGURRAN

to a 13-stone marathon runner. Mike said: "It's great because I've been able

"It was a huge shock to the system to run and agony as my saggy skin bounced all over the shop.

DAILY STAR SUNDAY, September 9, 2007 25

Incredible Shrinking Man

by ANDY LEA

MEGA-DIETER Mike Hare has gone from a 27-stone blubber mountain to a 12-stone distance runner – but no one believes him.

So the former fast food junkie has to carry an old photo of himself when he leaves the house so friends and work pals can recognise him.

Dad-of-four Mike, 53, said: "If I see someone I haven't seen for a while, they ask, 'Do I know you?' It happens a lot and I get a buzz out of it!"

Mike changed his ways after a car accident in 2005. He said: "I had to be cut out of the wreckage. It was like I'd got a second chance."

He ditched the junk meals and started cooking for himself with stir fries and fresh meat and veg. "All I've done is take a little more care of what I eat," he said. Now he'll line up for the Great North Run on September 30 in aid of The Prostate Cancer Charity.

But Mike isn't just a celebrity in his home town of Peterborough, Cambs. His "Incredible Shrinking Man" website has had 117,000 hits from others with weight problems.

He said: "I've got 'before' and 'after' photos on my sponsorship card but people still find it hard to believe I'm the same person."

Sponsor Mike at his website www.tism.co.uk

NOW 12 stone

THEN 27 stone

Wednesday, Septe

Ma Mi

THE self-proclai shrinking man staggering 15 sto years is now pre gruelling half-ma

It was a sudden which kickstarted M ishing transformati shedding his 27-and-

Mike was 50 when the wreckage of a ca treatment for mir decided to change h advantage of his seco

He cut out the mo chocolate, burgers, fr and tried to eat as mu vegetables as he coul

The father-of-four a Xenical tablets, whi from absorbing food the medication when enough not to need fa

With the weight s Mike took his mo regular trips to the gy

Mike, who lives in centre and works business, said: "No outside my comfort and never set foot in places. I was self-cons this soon faded.

"I was pleasant to what the gym facilities, and

NEAR-DEATH exp e left Mike Hare low of his former nd he couldn't delighted.

REAL LIFE WE LIVE IT

Before the amaz

ion Marathon

a RUN

sage from Peterborough Hare, who went from never e step to competing in a in the space of six months. stem Run 2008 will take place

you've ever ent doing and tho thing to do, th your life thinki do it."

Mike has bee has already c

Newsro...

ing the pounds antastic cause

by Mariann

THE Great Eastern Run which takes place on October 12 this ... has signed a new recruit ... to take

How to lose 15 stone In Two Years

Mike Hare, known as the incredible shrinking man, talks to S-Xpress reporter Clark Chapman about his amazing journey.

Imagine a single moment changing your life. Imagine those few seconds when life seems to be slipping away. For one man this became a reality. Mike Hare, 53, was your ... hard working father until one October evening ...

...e smoke coming from ... when I thought I was a ... of the wreckage and I even ...ed with me that night, I

He decided to complete... ...alise I couldn't keep liv... ...ome accustomed to. I ... a second chance ...o throw it away." ... of action was to ...amatically. He visit... ...ecrous occasions ...ike's head. "During ... t I actually ... went to see my doc... ...ccasion and he ... me doing a run ...thing inside of ... wanted to do it.

... a local fun ...oyed the ... his heart set ... Run for his ... was not ...d famous

... half of a ... o my ... people ... mine ...nkfully ... meant ... ed ... every

...s jour... never

anticipated how popular my training blog would becom... 132,000 hits. I couldn't believe it."

The big day had arrived, the months of hard work and d... about to be tested in the largest half marathon in the wor... on the verge of realising his goal. Somehow the BBC had ... Mike's amazing story and they wanted to interview him.

"I was about to run in the biggest half marathon in the wor... race was due to set off for 10.40am but due to the mass numbers I wasn't expected to reach the starting line until about an hour later. I was then given a pass which allowed me access to the front of the race, the BBC wanted to interview me." Mike was surrounded by a few household names.

"I was being interviewed by Jonathan Edwards and literally standing six feet from Paula Radcliffe. I told Jonathan about my chosen charity and I remember saying 'during this conversation someone will be diagnosed with prostate cancer.' I feel I did my best to represent the charity."

Mike completed the Great North Run in two hours 24 minutes, beating his expected time by quite a margin.

After we talked about the enormous achievement of Mike completing the race I asked him about how he managed to not only lose such a vast amount of weight but also gain such fitness.

"I have to be honest, it's all about mental strength. I ate sensibly and healthily. I didn't use the traditional method of using dietal processes, I just ate less but healthier. Success breeds success."

I also asked Mike about the obesity epidemic sweeping through the UK. He was brutally honest with his respo... general, if people don't put so mu... gain weight. It's as simple as ... calories and you int... and vice versa ... choices."

AFTER

hon man sheds 15st

By MARK PEARSON
mark.pearson@peterboroughtoday.co.uk

...oming everyone was.

...is such a change, I used to have a ...ntary life, sitting at my desk doing ...omputer work, but now I am either ...ing or at the gym."

... started to find that people had ...ulty recognising him, and was ...g encouragement from his doctor, ...e exercise paid dividends on his ... pressure.

...ends started to call him the ...dible shrinking man, a name ... inspired his website and daily

... regularly updates his blog and ...te with what he is doing, and both ...ed with messages of support.

...ier this year, his doctor suggested ...e part in a half marathon, so ...signed up to The Great North ...which takes place on September

...dded: "I have been training very ... and this includes doing three ... runs during the summer."

...e plans to raise £2,000 for The ...te Cancer Charity when he does ...n. He said: "Over the past few ... have lost a number of friends ...quaintances to this killer, and ...nter one of the guys I holiday ...ch year had a narrow escape."

... find out more, or to make a ...n, visit www.tism.co.uk

Mike's diet changes

BEFORE

- Breakfast – would normally skip, and eat lots of snacks and drink cups of coffee before lunch.
- Lunch – hot cheese and bacon baguette.
- Dinner – decent meal – normally with a second helping, followed by a large sweet pudding (rhubarb crumble) with icecream.
- Sugary drinks, coffee and snacks until bedtime.

NOW

- Breakfast – high fibre cereal or toast, grapefruit juice and coffee.
- Snack – cappuccino and a banana, or dried fruit and nuts.
- Lunch – chicken salad sandwich, a few cherry tomatoes and fresh fruit.
- Dinner – wshite meat or fish, fresh vegetables, wholemeal pasta or a jacket potato. Yoghurt and a coffee.
- With the odd egg and bacon sandwich as a treat.

SUPER SLIMMER: Mike Hare, left, before he lost an amazing 15st, and training for his first half-marathon, above. (7PF0914707/7PF0914732)

Pictures: PAUL FRANKS

PRIDE FILE

Runner's head start

...RAISER got a ...start at

SHED EQUIVALENT OF 44 BIG BAGS OF S...

15

Saturday,

15 stone..no... the maratho...

FAT'S UNBELIEVABLE . . . Mike shed a whopping 15 stone and took up long-distance running

ferent perspective of the river, meadows, country park and nature reserves.

"I could feel myself smiling. I hadn't felt that good in ye...

"One day I went ... that I dr...

fit, but I was astonished wh... went for my check... doctor ...

JUNK ...

LEFT
Left to right: Para Handy, TISM, Poseur and Auld Thai Tam at the end of the Great North Run, September 2007.

BELOW
The Realbuzz bloggers…

BELOW
Left to right: Number Two, Number Four, Mike, Number Three and Number One at the end of the Great North Run, September 2007.

BACKGROUND
A few of Mike's medals and memorabilia.

BELOW
The Flora London Marathon, April 2008.

After completing the Rome marathon, March 2009.

CHAPTER THIRTEEN

HALF THE MAN I USED TO BE

THE VERY NEXT DAY AFTER THE MANCHESTER RACE I WAS BOOKED IN FOR my usual visit to the doctor, and he assured me that all was fine ahead of the impending visit to see the surgeon. When I got back afterwards and did the maths to convert his kilos into real weights, I realised that he had finally confirmed that my weight was officially 12 stone 11.8 pounds. I had actually beaten my target of 12 stone 12 pounds – that figure I had a vague recollection of being at one stage when I was at school. I had never really thought it would be possible, had thought maybe I would get a bit close to it, but here I was – ACTUALLY AT MY TARGET WEIGHT. I was staggered, and unbelievably delighted with myself, I had actually done it!

To say I was pleased with myself is perhaps one of the biggest understatements I could possibly make. I was ECSTATIC! I really didn't get much sensible work done that day – I simply couldn't concentrate. It had taken me 2½ years from way back in January 2005 when I found out I weighed 27 stone 8 pounds (386 pounds) to get to 12 st 12 lbs (180 pounds). I had lost 14 st 10 lbs (206 pounds), and when I was playing the numbers through my head the old Beatles song 'Yesterday' kept popping up – you know the line,

"Suddenly, I'm not half the man I used to be . . . "

It was absolutely true, I actually weighed LESS THAN HALF of what I used to weigh. How mad was that? I really DID deserve the nickname The Incredible Shrinking Man. After all, I had now shrunk to less than half my size. I got quite carried away with checking numbers – I even got the tape measure out to do some checking. *Just so that I would know!*

I had lost 7 inches from my neck.

I had lost 23 inches from my waist. (If I held the skin flap out of the way!)

I had gone down a shoe size – now who would have ever thought that would happen?

I checked through the remnants of my old wardrobe, and my hats were too big for me now, and slipped right down over my eyes. Even my gloves were loose and uncomfortable. In fact I realised that I only had two things that still fitted me from my old wardrobe – my ties and my belts. OK you might think that's cheating a bit – I had to make new holes in the belts and cut a couple of feet off the ends – but nothing else fitted. It was almost symbolic really, like shedding the old appearance once and for all. I even realised, in this orgy of self-awareness and self-congratulation, that I was brushing my hair differently now and had allowed myself a small sort of goatee beard thing on my chin (I had always had a moustache, so it wasn't that big a deal). There was definitely some sort of psychological stuff going on to reinforce this whole *new image* thing in more ways than I had really focussed on, but it didn't feel like a bad thing at all. On the contrary, the *new package* felt damned good from the inside, and if anybody else really preferred the old look then they had better keep quiet and learn to live with it. This *new me* was here to stay!

I had a couple of really great runs during the week, while the euphoria stayed with me and lightened everything I did. I wasn't doing anything too drastic this week as I had a heavy weekend coming up, including having to face *Cardiac Hill* in the Thurlby 10k Race that Sunday. I'll never really know what on earth had possessed me to enter two 10k races on consecutive Sundays – it's not as if I was used to doing this sort of thing. Firstly I had to get through the Saturday task of driving over to Nottingham to load up the car and move Number Three from her digs over there back towards home. She had been working in Nottingham since deciding, after a full year of training at Queens Medical Centre in Nottingham University, that nursing was really not what she wanted to do for the rest of her life. Now she was finally moving back and had decided to move in with her boyfriend who had recently been provided with a very nice big bungalow attached to his work. So I had been elected to provide the transport, yet again. I had got used to this over the years, with various moves to and from universities, and was now an expert at loading vast amounts of rubbish (aka *But I need that, Dad*) into the car. That move went perfectly smoothly, and by Saturday evening all was quiet again and an early night was achieved.

Sunday dawned brightly and in no time I was off for the relatively short drive to Thurlby, about 15 miles north of Peterborough on the A15. This time I was meeting up with Sophie, a blogger who was studying modern languages at Durham University, and her boyfriend. Her folks lived not too far away, and the two of them had decided to come over to do the run when I had mentioned it in my blog. This was much more like the Deepings 10k, a local village race, principally comprised of members of the local running clubs, and a few privateers like Sophie, and I. My first surprise of the day came when I spotted Dr Ken in the small crowd milling around before the start. It turned out that he hadn't come to run, and certainly hadn't come to see me run, as he was as surprised to see me as I was to see him. He had actually come to watch and support one of his offspring in the 3k fun run, but it did provide the opportunity to discover that he had done some running himself in his younger days, right up to running the London Marathon. Maybe this finally explained why he had suggested that I do a run!

When the time arrived, all the runners trooped across to the far side of the playing fields and onto a residential road, where we were quickly lined up and sent on our way. The course wound its way through the houses for nearly a mile, before turning onto the road out of the village and up what Tom had called *Cardiac Hill* but which I now knew to be more correctly referred to us Strawberry Hill. Basically it headed out of the village in a more or less straightish line uphill for about a mile until it arrived at the foot of the radio mast. I had not previously realised such hills existed in this area until my research visit, having believed it to have been where the original architect of the universe had abandoned his Steam Iron when he realised that hills and mountains actually looked good. This damned hill just kept disappearing upwards, along with Sophie, her boyfriend, and most of the other runners. Luckily there was a fair smattering of more sedate individuals so that I certainly didn't end up feeling lonely as I finally crested the top to what were pretty stunning views, to be honest.

From there we turned left, and the route basically formed a large square through some pretty little hamlets and farms dotted about otherwise extremely rural lanes. The contrast to running through the highs and lows of inner city Manchester the previous week could not have been more marked. Scenically, they were at the two opposite ends of the spectrum, but the Manchester route had not been without its charms, and had been significantly enhanced by the tremendous support of the residents all the way round. Here, with the tail end of the field strung out along the country lanes, most of the time the only observers were dumbstruck wildlife and the odd cow. Nevertheless it was a thoroughly enjoyable run, and on the basis that *what goes up, must come down* (the race finished back at the playing fields where it had started), once we had passed the radio mast the rest of the route was primarily gently downhill.

The final mile back into the village and round towards the finish area was buoyed up by an increasing numbers of spectators providing encouragement from their front gardens. The last few hundred yards were almost crowded, and it was good to finish to a hearty and well-meant round of applause from the previous finishers. This is another delightful aspect of these smaller local races. Virtually everyone stays around the finish area until the last runners are home, and everyone is given the same welcome and congratulations on finishing from the first to the last finisher. There is no elitism as a general rule, just a broad camaraderie that encompasses everyone. My time was a little quicker than at the Deepings 10k at 66 minutes 16 seconds, which was a good performance given that damned hill. For the record, I finished 143 out of 154 finishers, so once again I wasn't last! The reward here was my first race medal, given to everyone who finished rather than a T-shirt or a mug. I really liked having that hung round my neck and being able to wear it while we had a chat and a cup of coffee; I decided not to chance the sausages or burgers that were being enthusiastically barbecued by the local scout troop.

A couple of pictures later (with medals), Sophie and Chris had to hit the road back to Northamptonshire, and so I hit the road back, which luckily, again, went right past the gym where I stopped off for a melt in the steam room, and a relax in the Jacuzzi before heading home. It was while I was bubbling gently in the spa that it occurred to me that my next race really *was* The Great North Run, and that it was only 3 months away. I also realised that it would mean, effectively, doing the run I had just done at Thurlby, then doing it again for a second lap, then doing another mile just to round it off. Not only was it feeling more real, but the prospect was becoming more daunting by the minute too. It certainly gave a new edge to the training runs from that point.

As the timescales got shorter and shorter towards the big run, it was time to get a little more serious about the sponsorship side of things. I had got my place in the Great North Run by being given a *Bond Place* by The Prostate Cancer Charity as I wanted to run for them.

Most of the larger charities have these *bond places* for the big, really popular runs that are oversubscribed, and they are a strange partnership between race organisers, charities and the runners. I had not known anything about these until getting mine, but had immediately cottoned on to what it was all about. Most races around the world are simply *enter and run* races, but there a good many now where more people want to run than the race organisers can accommodate. The few runners who can get the *qualifying times* get automatic entry to most races, but the rest have to apply through a random ballot, which is usually hugely oversubscribed. It has now become usual for race organisers to *sell* a large number of entries to the race to the charities, at a huge premium to normal entry cost, in some cases as much as ten or more times the normal fee. This creates substantial extra revenue for race organisers, and allows charities to effectively ask runners to *bid* for entries. This has now become regularised so that charities set *tariffs* for their places for different races, according to the type of race and likely demand for places from runners who are not lucky in the general ballot. To obtain the place, runners have to sign a *bond* to the charity for the amount of the tariff, so that if they fail to raise the required amount they make up the shortfall to the charity themselves.

My *bond* tariff for the Great North Run was £400 that year. For races like the London Marathon the tariff is usually something around £1500 to £2000, depending on the charity. So I was *on the hook* for £400, which was not too daunting really. I was introduced by The Prostate Cancer Charity to a marvellous website called www.justgiving.com which allowed anyone to easily set up a personal page for sponsors to make payments online, direct to your chosen charity, in your name. This saved me the bother of extracting cash from people, and also meant I could send out an email to everyone I knew with a link to the web page, and be able to raise sponsorship from donors I might not otherwise see face to face. So I set up my page, set my target at the required £400, and sent off a batch of emails to all and sundry. Now bearing in mind that a lot of these people would have not have seen me for a year or two, and probably had no idea that I had been on *Project TISM*, I made sure I put a *before and after* photo on the webpage. This made me pretty certain that the shock factor would probably mean some pretty good donations, at least, once people had recovered their breath! As predicted, it had the desired effect, and in the first few days I had to quickly edit my target upwards as I didn't want anyone thinking they didn't need to donate any more as I had hit my target. Within the first couple of weeks of it going live I had to raise it again to £1,000 to keep ahead of the game and I could already stop worrying as I had exceeded the bond tariff of £400. (Before the race took place I actually had to raise it to £2,000.)

All this, plus the training, kept me occupied until the appointment with Mr Malata, the Consultant Reconstructive Surgeon. As the day approached it suddenly dawned on me that the appointment was actually on Friday the 13th July, and immediately I set about persuading myself that I was not in the least bit superstitious. This was just a pure coincidence, and Friday 13th was just an urban myth, an *old wives tale* sort of thing. This time I was not going to be unlucky again, but we were going to *do the business* without a problem.

When I was finally ushered in, his first reaction was delight that I had clearly gone away and done as I was bidden. He got the nurse to check my weight, and confirmed that the BMI target had been duly beaten, and we could go ahead and get this done. At this point I mentioned that, although at the previous meeting I had said that my thighs were not a problem, with the extra weight loss and the running they were now getting significant loose rolls of skin down the insides of the thighs. He took a look and said that they were indeed worth doing in his opinion, and he would be delighted to do them, although it was not something the local NHS Primary Care Trust would normally fund. He did say he would talk to my doctor and discuss putting me up as a special case for their consideration. We then went on to discuss the detail of the operation, and he said that he had never seen such an extreme case, and it would be good to do this for me. He looked at his file, and said that he would need me in for the operation in about 8 weeks.

Disaster! I hastily explained that I was, in fact, running the Great North Run for the Prostate Cancer Charity on 30th September, and could we possibly arrange to do it in such a way as it didn't interfere with this important part of *The Project*. He was brilliant, and even asked if I was planning for a little break after the run to recover properly. When I explained that I was actually supposed to be going down to Spain with the boys for our annual outing a week or two after the run, he said that he would be delighted to perform the operation as soon as I got home from Spain. RESULT. Simple as that! I was to have a *Fleur-de-Lys Paniculectomy*, more or less whenever it suited me. Apparently he had originally been intending to do a simpler operation, just slicing me across the stomach, but I had now lost so much weight, and there was more loose skin than he had seen before, so he was going to do the first slice and then add another vertical slice up to my breast bone. At this point I ducked out of the conversation as it was all getting a little bit too graphic and I was intending to leave the worrying till the night before the operation when it was too late to back out. He finished by congratulating me on what he described as an extraordinary achievement, and assured me that he would write straight away to my doctor about the thighs, and that I should go and see him soon. Making the appointment was the first job as soon as I got back to the flat, as it could sometimes take a fortnight if I was fussy and actually wanted to see my own doctor.

The next couple of weeks were fairly quiet on most fronts, and I got some good runs in around Ferry Meadows. One of my early acquisitions on the running equipment front had been a Garmin Forerunner 305 – basically a fancy piece of kit which was a satellite system on your wrist, with the addition of a heart rate monitor band which you strapped round your chest. This gave me a read out on my wrist of time, speed, distance and heart rate, and was extremely useful for my training. I no longer had to plan where I should run to get the right distance, but could just run where I fancied on the spur of the moment, and be able to see the distance in metres as I went, and could check my speed at any time. After each run, I could plug it into the computer and get a map of where I had run, and also check the statistics for the run, and compare it to previous runs to see if I was making any improvements.

When I had mentioned on my blog that I had now acquired a Garmin, I was immediately advised that it was a bloggers tradition to have a nickname for it. I now realise that this is because it is a totally invaluable part of running training, as it monitors you on the run, gives you accurate time and distance, keeps you on your pace, and tells how you are improving. I thought long and hard about a nickname over the next few runs. In the end my sense of history, and perhaps some strange hidden sense of the future, prompted me to call it *Dippi*. Now I realise that this sounds very shallow and frivolous at first glance, which also adds a bit to the fun. I had begun to think of this piece of kit as the *heart* of my running training, and remembered that the very first marathon was run, according to Greek legend by a soldier called Phidippides. *Dippi* is therefore a simple extract of the heart of PhiDIPPIdes!

On one run, when I had decided to drive out to a particular car park and go for a shortish run round one of the lakes, rather than run the extra 2 miles each way to get out there in the first place, I switched on the Garmin in the car and was waiting for it to pick up the satellites, when I noticed that it was showing my resting heart rate as 39 beats per minute. Now I know that with the weight loss, and all the cardiovascular exercise I was doing, I now had a relatively low heart rate, but this was quite seriously low, so I started the record button just to get it on the print out before I started the run. Once I got back I checked the stats, and printed off the heart rate chart so that I could show the doctor when I saw him next.

The training plan I was working to said that I should be up to 8 miles in July, but, as I had already done at least one run of 8 miles in June, I hit 9 miles a couple of times, and then just before I saw the doctor again I did my first run of 10 miles. At this point I was now two full months ahead of schedule, and according to all the advice on the Great Runs website I was now at the point where I could successfully do the Great North Run. Strangely, when training for a half marathon or a marathon, apparently it is not necessary to train right up to the full distance, because the crowds of supporters and the other runners, and the atmosphere, will carry you the extra few miles on the day. By know I had also decided that I would definitely NOT run the full distance before the race, just so that the actual race itself would really be the very first time I ran a half marathon.

So, when I saw Dr Ken on the 26th I was in a pretty good mood. Training was going well, and ahead of schedule; the surgeon was going ahead with the operation at last; I had hit my target weight. We discussed the operation, and also the potential for doing the thighs. He repeated what the surgeon had said about it not normally being something that would be done, but he was perfectly happy to write to the Primary Care Trust and ask if they would fund it in my case. I then told him about the heart rate, and showed him the chart I had printed off. I should have realised what this would mean, without thinking about it, but it hadn't occurred to me. I was immediately told to book another ECG to have my heart checked over again. Apart from that everything else was fine.

Then he started to assess the current position. He told me that, although he enjoyed seeing me most months, I had long since stopped taking any prescriptions and that I clearly (subject to the ECG) had absolutely nothing wrong with me at all. Therefore, once I had seen him with the results of the ECG, he really didn't need to see me regularly any more.

Fair enough, I thought.

August started with a totally weird experience; a rugby international at Twickenham *IN AUGUST*! They were having some special pre-world-cup friendly internationals, and because of the time of year tickets had been unusually easy to get hold of – Twickers wasn't even completely full. Going to the old place to watch England on a glorious summer Saturday afternoon was almost surreal, certainly seeing England beat Wales 62 points to 5 was totally surreal! The day was great fun all round, as I had got hold of enough tickets to be able to take Number Three's boyfriend along. All my girls have been there a time or two – singing 'Swing Low, Sweet Chariot' in a crowd of 80,000 at Twickenham is one of those things that has to be *ticked off on life's shopping list*. He was a firm rugby fan and played at university, but had never been there, so we put that right as soon as we could. He was also introduced to the delights of the steak baguettes produced by the South African barbecue which is always set up in someone's front garden about 300 yards from the stadium on the right as you walk up from the station. This is an absolutely integral part of the day – one on the way to the ground, and another on the way back.

Now I know that you will be thinking '*How does a barbecued steak in a white baguette fit the diet plan?*', and you would normally be right to question it – and even more right to question the second one on the way back, and probably the beers in the ground too if I had mentioned them! This can all be safely covered by reference to the *special mantra* I mentioned earlier during the Crete trip:

Feed the body correctly – but don't forget to 'feed the soul' now and again.

Although certain things might not fit the perfect diet plan, your quality of life goes down too much to bear without them. Every now and again you have to make sure you have a treat, if for no other reason than that it makes you *feel good*. Call it whatever you like, but essentially it is what I call *soul food*, whatever it is. So every now and again, when tickets could be had, this was a day out which simply HAD to bow to our long family traditions, and it always *feels good*.

The following Saturday was probably even more expensive, but unique and very special. Number Three's 21st birthday was only a few days away, and this was the night when we could all be together for a meal out. As was always the case, she had a free choice of where she wanted to have the meal (dangerous, I know, but what the heck? They're only 21 once!). Unsurprisingly she chose the place where over the years we had celebrated most of these types of event – the floating Chinese Restaurant on the river in the middle of the City. We'd probably been going there off and on for something like 15 years, and had never had a poor meal, and I know the girls all love the place. The whole family were there, and of course her boyfriend, and I had even been persuaded to invite the boyfriend's parents too – a great couple that we had bumped into a few times over the years through school and always got along with well. We had a great night, and I even managed to get a photo or two of all four girls *dressed for a night out* – a distinct rarity now with them starting to scatter around the country.

It had been a hectic few weeks, with so much going on, and the autumn was starting to hold the promise of bringing *The Project* to a finish. With the run being done, and the surgery now booked, it looked as if I might finally be able to draw a line under things and declare *The Project* successfully completed. How little did I know?

On the Sunday I went for a great 10½ mile run on a very hot sunny morning. Normally I would have waited till late afternoon when it was starting to cool off a bit, but I had realised that on the day of the race I wouldn't have that choice. So now I was trying to go for a longer run at 11:00 on Sunday morning each week, just to get used to doing it so it wouldn't hold any nasty surprises on the big day. On the Monday I packed my bags and my laptop computer, and headed for the airport last thing in the evening to be ready for a very early flight on Tuesday morning. Even though I would be going there with the boys in October, after the Great North Run, I was off to Spain (well it's a lovely country) for 11 days for a summer holiday and another two new experiences I would never have contemplated before.

CHAPTER FOURTEEN

IN THE MEDIA

JUST AS I WAS GETTING READY TO HEAD OFF FOR THE HOLIDAY, I RECEIVED a letter which was a guarantee of leaving in exceptionally high spirits. The Primary Care Trust had considered my doctor's request for the thigh operation, backed up by the surgeon, and had immediately agreed to fund it. This was fantastic news, and I knew I was extremely lucky to be given this opportunity. I immediately sent the Trust an email with my thanks and appreciation.

Now I had been talking to The Prostate Cancer Charity about fund raising tips to help me get as much sponsorship money as possible for doing The Great North Run, and they were very keen on trying to get bits into your local paper wherever possible. We had some long chats about what the story might be, and their PR people had got involved as they decided that they rather liked my story so far, and thought it might get some good media interest. We hadn't done anything yet, as they thought it should only be tried nearer to the actual run when it was more topical, but they anticipated talking to some media seriously at the beginning of September. I had also begun to notice that I was getting a lot of questions on the blog now from people wanting to know how I had been losing the weight, and what my diet was, and all sorts of bits and pieces. It seemed that quite a lot of people were now taking an interest in my ramblings on the blog, and I had a feeling that this might increase if the PR people managed to get any articles printed, and that meant possibly lots more questions. So I had concluded that it would probably be a good idea to prepare a set of answers to most of the usual questions, that I could then *wheel out* when required. Then I finally realised that the only sensible solution was to make them available to anyone who wanted to see them, and that meant putting them on a little website. So I also now had to find a bit of time, and some peace and quiet, to get this done in time for anything that might happen with the press before the run, and that's why I took my laptop with me on holiday.

I was going down to Southern Spain and staying on Para Handy's new boat in a lovely little marina between Estepona and Gibraltar, and had already checked that there was a Wi-Fi service in the port. When he had upgraded his little speedboat to a serious six berth cruiser and the offer to stay on the boat was first made, I had decided that I would take the chance to do the three day intensive course run by a company down there and try to get my Day Skippers licence which is a legal requirement for anyone wanting to use a boat in Spanish waters. I had sailed racing dinghies to quite a high standard up until I left school, and graduated to offshore racing yachts at one stage. So I already had an excellent knowledge of boats, and safety on the water, although engines remained a mystery to me. It had been an awfully long time since I was on a boat, but once these things are ingrained in you they never completely go away. The boat I was staying on was a beauty, American designed and therefore roomy inside. It slept four easily and comfortably, (or six very close friends), with shower, toilet, galley and all mod cons, so was as good as a really big caravan. The interesting bit was the two corvette engines which drove her fast enough to water ski behind! So the holiday plan was a ten day break, staying on the boat, and doing the licence course over the first three days. *Chilling out* and doing the website on my laptop, and doing nothing much else for the rest of the stay, completed what had the appearance of an excellent plan. It was also a relatively cheap way of getting a great holiday somewhere very warm, in high season!

The course itself was very intense, one-to-one on the boat, everything from knots to navigation charts, machinery to man overboard drill. We even had to go on a night navigation exercise down the coast very late one night, which got quite exciting at the point when one of the engines failed about 3 miles offshore. It turned out not to be anything too serious, and was quickly put right in the light of day, but made for an interesting couple of hours limping back to home port in the dark. It was great to be able to do this course in the shadow of the Rock of Gibraltar, and with the promise of the company of dolphins at any time

– although I never saw one at all. I'm of the opinion that the dolphins off that part of the coast of Spain are closely related to a certain Scottish legendary water dweller! However I would have to say that the main thing I learned during those few days was that I still infinitely prefer a sail to an engine on a boat. A power boat attacks the waves, and bounces around on them, but a sailing boat cuts through the water and waves, and works with the sea at all times making a much smoother ride. The other significant difference was, having to call into the fuel station on the way out of the harbour, and spend a fortune to fill the fuel tanks so that you could watch the dials go back down before your very eyes if you really opened the throttles. The wind that powers a sailing craft is free; usually plentiful; you don't need to stop and collect some before leaving harbour; and if it gets a bit strong at times then you wouldn't be out in a power boat then either. Never mind, this was great fun, and I was grateful for the chance to use it both as a base, and for touring up and down the coast once I had my licence safely acquired.

With the course out of the way I set about learning how to design and create a website, fill it with interesting content, and make it *live* – which was a very new experience indeed. I'd hate to try to work out how many goes I had at it, but by the end of the holiday I had something which worked, and which seemed to do a nice simple job. It would at least be possible to mention it to people now, and hopefully save me the time of having to answer every question separately. More importantly, I could put the address for it on anything that went out to the media from The Prostate Cancer Charity. In between times I actually went out for a couple of runs between 3 and 4 miles long along the promenades that flanked the coast on either side of the port. I did not particularly like running in the full heat of high summer down there, and the few people that did appear to run regularly always did so at first light before the sun really got up steam. However, I was more used, on summer holidays, to seeing first light BEFORE I went to bed, rather than it being when I got up for a run, so I packed my running shoes away and forgot about them for the rest of the stay.

The other thing I realised when I got there was that once I had hooked up my laptop to build the website, I could also write up my blog. So this gave me the opportunity to try adding photos from my little digital camera too. Having grown up in an era when you got to see your holiday photos a week after you got home, provided the local camera shop developed them properly, it never ceases to amaze me that you can look at your photos on the camera screen instantly, and then put them into your computer and onto the internet so that anyone can see them anywhere. The thought that I could actually show the folks back home my holiday snaps, before I got home, would have been totally beyond comprehension 25 years ago. What was even more amazing was that here I was, sitting on a boat in a Spanish harbour, using a laptop computer to build a website, keep my blog up to date, and put some photos online. It appeared that you CAN teach an old dog new tricks after all – even an old *sea dog*!

Suntanned, relaxed, a qualified skipper and the proud owner of the wonderful new website www.tism.co.uk I finally headed back to Malaga Airport and the scrum they call Easyjet Check-in. A few hours later, sitting back at home, it was already becoming just a memory as the reality of five weeks till the big run started to hit home.

At this point I was brought face to face with a whole new reality surrounding what I was doing. When I was talking to the PR people at The Prostate Cancer Charity, I had sent off another email. At the time I was using my local Bannatyne's Gym, and had been a member there for over a year. The owner of this chain of gyms, Duncan Bannatyne of *Dragon's Den* fame on the TV, had been making some strong statements all over the media about *office obesity* and how people could lose weight if they exercised a bit more (in his gyms, I presume). I looked him up on the internet, found an email address and sent him off a quick précis of what I had done using his gym. I was, to all intents and purposes, living proof of what he was talking about, and wondered if he wanted to use me for a bit more publicity in return for some sponsorship. I hadn't expected to hear anything, but apparently his office had picked it up, sent it off to the chief executive of the gyms, who had passed it down the line and set up a meeting with me and the local manager. So when I got back I had to go in for this meeting, and see what could be sorted out.

The offer was quite clear and unequivocal. They wanted their public relations company to have use of my story, and to work with the charity too on anything they wanted to put out. They wanted to use my story for local and national publicity for the gyms, as they thought it was a terrific achievement, and especially wanted to do some things around the Great North Run. They especially wanted to arrange a photo session in the gym for some publicity work.

"OK, if I agree to all that, what are you offering me towards my sponsorship?" I asked, quite reasonably I thought.

The response was three things. First of all:

"Free membership of the gym for one month for you to raffle at work."

"I work alone, at home. The other guys I work with are miles away. This is no use to me."

Second thing: "Some bits from our shop to raffle at work."

"Which part of my previous response did you not understand?"

Third thing: "Buy yourself a running vest in town, and bring in the receipt and we will pay for it – provided we can have our name printed on the shirt to show up in all photos of you."

At this point I explained that I already had businessmen, and businesses, who had sponsored me for some very generous amounts, and I was not really wanting to explain to them that I had not put their names on my shirt when their generosity was so much greater. I also explained to them that I would, in fact, be running in the especially designed Prostate Cancer Charity running vest that they kindly gave to all their runners to help identify them on the race.

They were unwilling to discuss their extremely generous offer any further, and would not even entertain the idea of making even a small donation to The Prostate Cancer Charity, but would like to know when it would be possible to arrange for some photos to be taken in the gym.

I politely declined their overwhelming generosity, made my excuses and left. As soon as I could get on to my computer at home I diligently went through all my old blogs and carefully edited out all references to Bannatyne's gyms. Then I went through the website with a fine-toothed comb and edited out any references in there. I had resolved that they would never get any credit whatsoever for anything I had done, and since then I have made it a pre-condition of any writing or interviews that their name is not mentioned in any way with anything to do with me. I also resolved that when my annual membership came up for renewal I would be looking for another gym – and I did!

This episode did, however, start to make me realise that people might be interested in the story of what I had done. This was a very strange feeling, as it had been a very private and personal journey so far, and, apart from some friends being amazed, it had never occurred to me that there could be that sort of interest. Yes, I had received a lot of questions through the blog, and got to know a lot of new people through it. And I had thought it worth starting up the little website in case a local paper or two ran an article about people from the area doing the Great North Run. But here was the possibility that a big company wanted to get their public relations people using the story. This was almost instantly backed up by the PR team at the charity telling me that they wanted some photos of me because they had received *some interest* in the story, not that I knew what that really meant.

This all went on the back-burner for a while, as there were more important things going on. Every year the main theatre in Peterborough, the Key Theatre, puts on a summer musical for a week with a cast of the best local young talent. It is a highly popular show each year, and sells out the 450 seats practically every night. This year, Number Four had one of the lead roles in *Into the Woods* – a show I hadn't seen before, which is a clever weaving together of all the classic pantomime fairy takes such as *Cinderella*, *Red Riding Hood* and *Jack and the Beanstalk*. So for the last week in August everything was dominated, as it rightly should be, by the show. I finally got to see it on the last night, with all the family, and was as proud as ever as she lit up the stage in her usual style. She had been involved with local drama and musicals for years, and this was the second time she had performed a major role in the summer show and she didn't disappoint. Mind you, it was fun meeting up with so many of the local theatre folk we had run into now and again over the years and watching their faces as they slowly realised who I was, and how different I was. But I tried to keep a low profile on this occasion, there could only be one star in the family that night, and it certainly shouldn't be me.

All of a sudden it was now September, and the Great North Run was *this month*. It had seemed such a long way off when the doctor had said "You should do a run" but now I could count the days, and would very soon be counting the hours. I kept to the training schedule as much as

I could, and even managed to get in an extra run or two even though I knew perfectly well that it was too late to make any significant improvements now. I had trained according to Masochistic Mickey's master plan, and I was ready. In fact I started to watch out for myself more than ever, as there was no way I wanted to get injured now. The latest email bulletin from The Great Run people had reassured everyone that if you could run 10 miles reasonably comfortably by now, then you would be absolutely fine on the day. It also, by the way, asked if anyone running the race had any interesting stories to tell, as they were always looking for stories for the website, and their newsletters. So I thought that I would send off an email, just in case they didn't have many and needed something badly enough to use a simple *guy loses some weight story*.

About this time, the Prostate Cancer Charity people also sent out a press release to their normal contacts, and, it seems, spoke to a few of the local media around my area too. The result astonished me, but to be honest it was also a lot of fun, and shyness had never been one of my strong points anyway. For the next three weeks I was in almost daily contact with Nikki, my main contact at the charity, as she reported conversations, and set up things for me to do. The first coverage was a full page article in the *Daily Star Sunday*, on the 9th September, and it even mentioned my website address. I knew that this article was coming out, because *The Star* had arranged to send out a photographer to get some photos of me in my running gear for the article. I had made sure that I was wearing my Prostate Cancer Charity running vest for the photos. They also put in the article that, in the six months since I had started that simple little blog, as advised by the Great Run people, there had been 117,000 visits by people looking at my blog. What they didn't know is that I had only finally let the website go live to the world two days before the article, so that they could see it, and check it was there before mentioning it. By the 13th, mainly because they mentioned it in the article, the website had received nearly 700 visitors, and I began to worry about what I had said on there now that I was faced with the stark reality that 700 people had been reading my ramblings on there.

Nikki was delighted, as were her colleagues at the charity, as apparently they had never been able to get a mention of the charity in that particular national paper before, and now they had a mention in the article, and their name and logo big and bold on the photo of me. It appeared that I was becoming quite popular at the charity headquarters, and as a result of the article they began to get more interest in the story.

Unfortunately, I also encountered another side of the commercial interest in my story. I had put a facility on my website for people to leave comments if they wished, and some had been kind enough to leave some very complimentary messages. In case anyone was asking any questions, I had taken to the habit of checking the site on a daily basis as I didn't particularly want to upset anyone by appearing to ignore them. A couple of days after the *Daily Star* article appeared, some messages were left on the website for me from some press agencies offering to pay me for my story provided that I signed a contract with them allowing them exclusive rights, and leaving phone numbers to call them. These were right there, in full public view, on my website. I was furious, and immediately removed them of course. This made me check the site even more often for a while, because this sort of thing was totally out of order as far as I was concerned. Did they not realise that I was doing all this because of running for The Prostate Cancer Charity, and that any publicity should benefit them, not me?

While this was all going on, I had to pop to the surgery for the ECG the doctor had suggested, as a result of the heart monitor results I had shown him. Secretly, I think he wanted one last check that everything was as good as he thought before the actual race. So I lay there as usual hooked up to wires attached (with funny little sticky pads) to every part of my anatomy. Also as usual, the nurse declined to comment on the results, saying that it was not up to her to interpret it, but the doctor. Finally I saw the doctor a couple of days later to hear that there was absolutely nothing wrong with the results, all was fine. So I was cleared to get on and do the race without any worries at all.

During the last 2 weeks before the run I had some photos taken for an article in the local daily paper, the Peterborough *Evening Telegraph*, and they wrote a really good supportive article too. I also found myself in the studios of both the local BBC Radio station, and Hereward Radio – the local independent radio station, doing interviews about the weight loss and the run coming up. The commercial station just recorded a lot of stuff in a back room there, and then fitted extracts around the music and news bulletins. On the other hand, the BBC Radio interview was done live on air, and I was inside the studio chatting live to the presenter. If you ever feel low on adrenaline, just try doing a live, unrehearsed interview with the extra knowledge that a good proportion of your friends and family are listening in.

My email about my story to the Great Run people in response to their appeal for stories also got a reply, which ended up with a piece being written for their next email newsletter which went out to all runners and supporters. It was a very nice, complimentary piece, with a couple of photos. It also contained a link to the BBC local website for the North East where they had set up a page in their Great North Run section all about me! This was all getting quite fun now, and it was certainly bringing people to look at the website, and there were a lot of new visitors to my blog as a result of the email newsletter. But I was still managing to get my training in most days, and it was all overlaid with the strongest motivation of all now to make sure I finished the run well. The papers and radio stations all wanted me to contact them after the run with my result, so that they could do follow up articles, and the fear of having it splashed over the papers and radio that I had failed to finish was the worst nightmare possible right now.

In the end the final week dawned, and I started to *taper* my training. The accepted wisdom in the running world is that during the final week before a major run you tail off your training runs down to the bare minimum, to preserve as much energy for the big day as possible. Also for the last couple of days you are supposed to *carb* load ready for the run, although I think this should really only apply to the longer races like half marathons and full marathons. This is all about making sure that you eat really energy intense foods immediately prior to a really big run. The favourite of nearly all runners is pasta, and it is an absolute must the night before a race as an extra insurance policy against *hitting the wall*. Even elite runners *carb load* and take energy drinks and energy gels during marathons, because this is a factor for everyone.

So there I was on the Thursday, eased right down on the training, going through all my kit and stuff I would need for Newcastle, as I had decided to go up on the Friday. The plan was that I could have all day on the Saturday to relax and watch the various events put on for the occasion along the quayside – they have some short runs on the Saturday for the junior age groups, the *mini* Great North Runs, and they also have some elite athlete short races too like The Great North Mile. I also wanted to spend a fair bit of time at the *Expo* to which all runners were invited, and where many of the bloggers from the Realbuzz website had arranged to meet up on the Saturday afternoon. By now my race pack had arrived, with my number to pin on my vest, and telling me that I was to start in Zone J as indicated by my original estimated time of 2½ to 3 hours. What this actually meant in real terms was that I was starting very near the back, as I expected and anticipated, and the pack warned me that it would probably take about 40 minutes from the starting gun for me just to get to the start line with the crowds of runners in front.

For those who have never got close to a race like this, I should mention that in my race pack was also my *chip*. This is a natty little device used in all of the larger races nowadays, which you lace onto one of your running shoes. It sends out a tiny signal with your unique running number which is picked up by *sensor mats* on the road at the start and finish, and it is this that determines your personal time for the race, rather than suddenly finding that you are already 40 minutes slower than the other guys as you cross the start line. This technology is an absolute must when you are trying to organise a race with 50,000 entrants. Funnily enough they now also put extra sensors down along the route here and there at key distances, and if a runner misses being *counted* by the system at any point then they are disqualified. Anyway, all this stuff had to be packed, or I wouldn't even be able to enter the starting zone.

But Thursday had the biggest surprise of all waiting up its sleeve to catch me completely unawares. During the morning I had a phone call from a young lady who told me she was from the BBC, and asked me if I was aware that the BBC were broadcasting live from Newcastle on Sunday, covering the whole of the Great North Run. They would start broadcasting live on BBC1 at about 9:30, and run right through to 1:30 with coverage of all elements of the race.

All the really big world class events like this are always split up into three starts. First to go is the wheelchair race as these athletes really do travel at phenomenal speeds and mixing them up with runners would be a recipe for disaster. The second start a few minutes later is for the Elite Women's Race, which includes all women runners who have achieved the special qualifying time for the distance. They are sent off separately so that they can have a proper race, watched closely by the TV cameras, without becoming swamped by the men's race. About half an hour later the Elite Men line up at the start, with everyone else, male and female, who hasn't achieved the qualifying times for the Elite races penned up behind them in ranks according to expected speed. The exotic costume runners in their Rhino Heads, Sumo Wrestlers and any other strange and wonderful outfits are usually required to start at the back. This third start is known as the Men and Masses Start.

I confirmed that I did indeed know all of this as it had all been in the latest email newsletter from the organisers, but politely enquired why on earth she was phoning everyone to tell them when we all knew already.

"I'm not phoning everyone, Mike, I'm just phoning you. We would like you to appear on *Grandstand* before the start of the race for a live interview about your weight loss and your run, if you will agree."

Dammit – another of those moments when you know perfectly well what you want to say, but the words simply don't come out, and you are left feeling like an idiot, and knowing that she is probably thinking *Why would we want to interview someone with a speech impediment on live TV? I could lose my job here!*

After what seemed to me like an age, I managed to regain the power of coherent speech, and she seemed not to notice the incredibly long silence before I was able to agree. She asked me where I was staying, and I gave her the address of the hotel I had booked, and she said there would be some instructions left at the hotel for me, with details of where to go and when to be there by. She also told me that she would provide me with a pass to get into the *front zone*, where they would be conducting the interviews. On further enquiry this meant I would have to go right to the front of the start area, next to Paula Radcliffe and the Ethiopian runners, and stand around with all the celebrity runners until I was interviewed. Obviously two important questions sprang straight to mind, so I just came right out and asked her,

"Can I warn my friends and family to look out for me on the TV?"

"Of course you can. Tell them you should be on live, at about 9:48."

"Brilliant. But will I then be sent back to Zone J, where I belong, ready for the start?"

"No way! You can stay up there, watch the wheelchairs, and the women's elite start, and then you can start with all the celebrities right at the front!"

"Oh, thanks." I lamely replied.

This now meant that the rest of the day was spent phoning all and sundry, putting a note on the website, posting a special blog, and generally losing the plot completely. The folks at The Prostate Cancer Charity were completely blown away by this turn of events, as it meant that their name, emblazoned boldly across the front of my running vest, was going to be out there on the telly for all to see. And all they ever wanted was more awareness of Prostate Cancer, and raising the profile of the charity which very rarely got prime BBC TV mentions. By now it was almost impossible to concentrate, but I finally managed to get all my kit laid out and checked, and do the rest of my packing. I filled in the back of my running number and got that safely packed too. On the back of the *bib numbers* for these big races there are a series of key medical, identity and contact questions, so that if a runner collapses during the race the first aid team can identify them, be forewarned of any key conditions, allergies or sensitivities which might influence any treatment, and have a phone number of your supporters at the race, and at home. Clever stuff really, and something I never realised till I got that race pack.

Sleep that night was hard to come by, as my blood stream appeared to be in the process of being replaced with pure adrenaline. Eventually I got to sleep, but my dreams were dominated by what I later found to be *normal* issues for anyone taking on this sort of challenge. You have the *I've woken up too late and missed the transport to the start* dream, and the *standing waiting for the gun to go off and realising that you have lost your chip* dream, and any number of variations on the theme of *unthinkable disasters that will stop you running, get you disqualified or ensure your name does not appear as an official finisher*. Somehow I did manage to get some rest, and arrived at the morning feeling good and ready to go. After a last couple of phone calls, and putting the finishing touches to my packing, I was locking up and walking to the station.

The journey to Newcastle was fairly smooth and quiet, and I spent most of it in a reflective mood. Here I was, just a couple of weeks short of three years from the car accident. Then I was 28 stone, and not fit enough to be trusted to even drive a car properly. Now here I was, 35 months later, 15 stone lighter, heading for Newcastle to run the Greatest Half Marathon in the World, chatting on the radio, having papers write about me, and shortly to be interviewed live on BBC presumably as some sort of example of people who can do this race if they put their mind to it. I smiled all the way to Newcastle, as I realised that, after perhaps a very long wait, life really was getting to be rather fun again in a most unexpected way.

CHAPTER FIFTEEN

THE GREAT NORTH RUN

THERE'S SOME STRANGE CHANTING GOING ON AHEAD, CAN'T MAKE IT OUT – like nothing I've ever heard before, yet deep down it has a familiar sort of ring to it. As we head towards the Tyne Bridge, with the other lanes of the motorway overhead creating a long dark tunnel, it starts again. "Oggy Oggy Oggy", and a thousand voices, including my own I realise, respond at full strength "Oi Oi Oi". The 'oggies' under the motorway flyover are one of the great 'runners only' moments of long distance running. No spectators can get down there, and it is as integral to the runners' experience of this unique race as any other single aspect of the day. The hairs really are standing up on the nape of my neck, and I feel excitement coursing through me as I pound the crowded road up towards the great icon of both the North East, and of RUNNING – The Tyne Bridge!!

There, as planned, on the left hand pavement by the start of the 'arch', screaming with excitement and almost the same degree of incredulity as currently envelopes my own soul, are my girls, watching me in The Great North Run. Absolutely no one who knew me would EVER have believed it. Here I was, running the Greatest Half Marathon in the World!

I arrived in Newcastle in high spirits, and got a taxi to take me to the hotel, which turned out to be a fair way out of the centre, on the Gateshead side of the River Tyne. This meant crossing the famous old Tyne Bridge, which I knew was going to be part of the route of the run, and I got shivers up my spine as we approached it and I saw the massive banners draped across the bridge advertising The Great North Run. When I got to the hotel and checked in, the young lady receptionist handed over a small package which she explained had been delivered for me only a few minutes before I got there. I couldn't resist ripping it open right there at the desk, and there it was – the all important pass, on a long strap, permitting me to access the *Start Area*. It also contained instructions to be at the start area for 9:00am, with details of who to report to, and their mobile phone number. Even if they decided not to do the interview in the end, at least I had my pass now and could get into the *Celebrity Runners Area*.

At some time that night, I'm sure I probably did get some sleep, but it was touch and go for a while. Once I had found the breakfast room on Saturday morning, negotiated the buffet, and checked with the staff there that they would indeed be providing a special early breakfast on Sunday for all the runners staying there, I headed off into Newcastle on the bus. Way too keyed up for anything sensible now, I decided to have a look around the city centre before heading in the general direction of the river. I had a vague idea of where the *Expo* was supposed to be set up on the south side of the river, and that there were also the events on the Quayside, so I knew I would find it somehow. There had also been a lot of chat between the folks on the blogs arranging a general meet-up at the *Expo* during the afternoon, and I was really looking forward to turning some more virtual friends into real people. In the race pack everyone had received an entry pass to the *Expo*, and a ticket for a free bowl of pasta at the *Pasta Party*, so these were in my pocket, along with my camera, and my *Start Area* pass which I wasn't letting out of my sight now. In fact I caught myself checking it a couple of times, just to make sure I wasn't dreaming.

Eventually I found the approach to the Tyne Bridge, adorned with its giant banners for the race, and I walked across it full of anticipation about running across it the very next day. As I crossed, I realised that the Mini Great North Run was actually taking place on the quayside way down below the bridge, so I stopped to watch, and got a few pictures from a bird's eye view. Then it was time to find the *Expo*, and join the massive queue to get in. In all honesty it was a pretty poor affair, with very little in the way of interesting stands, considering the size of the potential audience of 50,000 runners and all their entourages. It was way past lunchtime by now, so I went straight through to the *Pasta Party*. The portions were really not very much, but I suppose that was only to be expected as they were free, after all. Luckily everyone had been given two tickets so that they could bring their partner or friend or whoever they wished, so by the time I had used my second ticket I had enjoyed a good lunch. One of the stands was giving away fruit, so desert was well catered for as well.

Strangely, as I really couldn't figure out the connection, the RFU had set up a large caravan in the outside area, and were showing some live international rugby matches, so I joined the small crowd to watch while I waited for the others to arrive. The rest of the afternoon passed all too quickly, as there really wasn't enough time to have a decent chat with everyone who turned up and introduced themselves around the group. The first person I met was Vicki, a Newcastle lass who I hadn't even thought would be there, but we instantly recognised each other from our photos on the blogs and it was a great way to get the afternoon going. From then on it was a flurry of mobile phone messages helping folks to *home in* on the gathering, followed by a couple of hours of adrenaline fuelled chatter about nothing much as we were by that time all getting just a little bit excited. But we were staying in a huge variety of places, as Newcastle itself cannot cope with the sheer numbers of people, so it was not long before we were heading off in all directions for a meal and an early night.

Back at the hotel I wandered into the bar with the intention of getting a light meal, and turning in very early. The transport to the race start at the Town Moor, which was part of the package I had booked through the race organisers, was leaving at around 7:30 in the morning, but it was not from the hotel but from somewhere about 20 minutes walk away. Apparently they would have a fleet of coaches at a central point catering for everyone staying in three or four hotels in that area, but that meant leaving the hotel by 7:00am, after having breakfast and getting kitted up for the race. However, once I got into the bar I was quickly swept up into a conversation with a few others there with similar plans for the evening, and I ended up eating with a guy about my own age who had done this race before, and many others along the way. He had come all the way up from the South Coast and was on his own as well, so I passed a great evening soaking up lots of tips about how to make sure I enjoyed myself.

The last thing I did was to make a couple of phone calls to York and Edinburgh, just to check the arrangements for the race. I might have been on my own on the Friday and Saturday, but I certainly wasn't going to be on the Sunday. My four daughters had all decided that they wanted to be there to see me run, as it was something that they had never ever thought would happen, and they wanted to support me. They couldn't get trains early enough on the Sunday morning from home to be in Newcastle for the start, so they had come up to York on the Saturday evening so that they could get an early train from there. They would have come up and stayed in Newcastle, but quite frankly the Great North Run weekend is a bonanza for Newcastle's hoteliers and guest houses and they throw the rate books out of the window and charge a fortune for rooms. In fact most central hotels will not take single night bookings, insisting you have to book for two nights at something like two to three times the normal room rates per night. Number Four, however, was in the process of deciding which universities to apply to, and Edinburgh University, which was on her short list, had organised their Open Day that Saturday. So she had been up in Edinburgh for a couple of days, having a look around, and staying with her godfather, Para Handy. The plan was that she would come straight down from Edinburgh on the Sunday morning, in the company of Para Handy, the Poseur and Auld Thai Tam who were all coming down for the race (Tam is another member of the FRA. His nickname stems from his finding out that his workmates call him Auld Tam, added to his regularly recounting tales of a long and interesting trip to Thailand a while back). What they had actually told me was that they were coming down with a large glass jar so that they could scrape my remains off the road – but what the heck, that's what friends are for, isn't it?

My final act before attempting sleep was to lay out everything ready for the morning, as I knew I would not necessarily be thinking totally clearly when I got up. It never ceases to amaze me how much stuff you have to lay out just to go for a run, but it always pays to be absolutely certain, as most of it is essential for a smooth race and good memories. So on the other bed, (a twin room for single occupancy does have its compensations), I laid out the following:

- **Running shoes**
- **Running socks**
- **Timing chip**
- **Velcro strap** for timing chip
- **Underpants**
- **Compression shorts**
- **Two waist band pouches** (one for camera and one for mobile phone)
- **Prostate Cancer Charity running vest**
- **Bib number**
- **Four safety pins** (for attaching bib number to vest)
- **Wrist sweatband**
- **Head sweatband**
- **Heart rate monitor on chest band**
- **Garmin** (stop watch thing)
- **Rucksack with clothes to throw on after race**
- **Energy drink**
- **Powdered recovery shake in bottle ready to make up**
- **Two bananas**
- **Baggage tag with race number on** (attached to rucksack)
- **Start Area Pass**
- **Race Instructions** (this race provides a little credit card sized fold out set, with start area, route and finish area maps which you can slip in a pocket)
- And last, but by no means least, **a bin liner** and a roll-on stick of ***Bodyglide***

The bin liner is an essential piece of kit for big races where you are going to be hanging around for a while before the start, and bearing in mind we had to leave the hotel at 7:00am and the race start was at 10:40am, there was going to be a lot of hanging around. You can wear a decent jacket up to the point where you hand your bag over to the baggage marshals, but from then on you can still have a long time to wait. The bin liner is therefore the ultimate throw-away wind and rain proof layer – just pop it over your head with holes pushed through for head, (and optionally for arms), and then when the gun goes just rip it off and throw it away. The alternative is to wear something you want to give to charity, and discard it at the start, as the race organisers collect it all and give it to local charities.

The *Bodyglide* is another matter entirely, and is mostly a requirement for men. Vaseline is an alternative, but I don't find it as effective over very long runs. It is to prevent, or minimise, *jogger's nipple*, arguably one of the most painful injuries that a runner can get. There is nothing worse than a hot sweaty running top constantly rubbing against your nipples every stride you take for mile after mile. It is not uncommon by any means to see runners finishing with large red stains on their vests from bleeding nipples – but generally a runner only does that once! So a specially-formulated, and long lasting, body lubricant grease is utterly essential for application before every run. Ladies tend not to suffer in this way, as sports bras tend to overcome the problem – or so I've been told! I had discovered *jogger's nipple* on one of my earlier long training runs, and although it's not necessarily too painful while you are running, it is sheer agony when the hot water hits in the showers afterwards.

Convinced that everything was now in order, I went to bed, having booked an early morning call, and set every alarm I could find and programme, as necessary. Somehow I actually managed to sleep like a log, right through till the alarms went off and the early morning call came through right on time.

At last, after months of preparation, the big day was here. It actually *was* Sunday 30th September 2007 – the day of The Great North Run.

I shot out of bed, had a very quick shave, and threw on a pair of jogging bottoms and a T-shirt and headed down for breakfast. Under normal circumstances hotel stays represented the only chance I ever got for a proper Full English (Cardiac) Breakfast, but that was definitely NOT a good idea on this occasion as heartburn or a heavy stomach did not fit well with running. I stuck to my pre-race routine of a small bowl of All-Bran, and some wholemeal toast, with orange juice and coffee. There were a lot of people wandering in for the early breakfast, but the room was quite subdued as everyone sat there contemplating what they had to do that day. I finished up, grabbed a banana from the fruit bowl, and headed off to my room to get my running kit on.

A few minutes later I was heading downstairs, and joining the trickle of people heading down the road towards the coach pick-up point, which turned out to be a lot further away than I had realised. I must admit to thinking that it might turn into a long, tough drag back to the hotel later on, but then I realised that after the race it wouldn't really matter. Once I got to the pick-up, I was directed onto the next coach in line, and in a couple of minutes we were on our way, with the coach more or less shrouded in reflective silence. As we approached the drop-off point at Town Moor the scale of the event began to become clearer. Up to that point it had just been a case of *the biggest half marathon in the world*, about 40,000 actual starters on the day (there are always a lot of *no-shows* due to injury or illness of either runners or members of their family), and other random facts. It was only when you started to see the queues of coaches waiting to disgorge their contents, and the long snake of runners writhing across the moor towards the motorway, that you started to get a feel for what that many people actually looked like. The next stage was negotiating the huge queues for the massed ranks of portaloos, and then on towards the bridge over the motorway as the baggage buses were on the other side, on a street that ran parallel to the motorway which itself formed the first section of the course. My plan was now very simple, pop over to drop off my bag, then get down onto the motorway and find the *Start Area*, which looked as though it would be the first *pen* you would come to. I knew I would be fine, as I still had almost an hour before I had to be there, and I could see the start line from where I was standing on the bridge.

Now the sheer scale of this thing really did hit home, as I walked up to the baggage buses. The instruction was to pass along the line of double decker buses being used for the purpose till you came to the next bus not yet full. Here you would show the baggage marshal that your bag tag was the same as your bib number, and they would stamp the number of the bus on the corner of your bib number, so that you could then get it back at the end of the race. Technically a simple proposition, but the buses didn't seem to start till about half a mile up the road, and countless numbers of them were already full, making me walk further and further away from the start line, through a huge throng of people, and queues for the many blocks of portaloos spaced out along the side of the road. By the time I finally got to the next *open* bus, dumped my bag, and got my stamp, I realised that I was actually going to be pressed for time to get back to the bridge, down onto the motorway, and find the right entrance through the huge fences along both sides that had been erected to keep the crowds of supporters at bay. It was quite a good warm-up as I tried to power walk through crowds, not staying quite as calm and collected as I had intended. But I made it with literally only seconds to spare, and the magic pass did its job of getting me past the security and into the relative peace, quiet and comparatively wide open spaces of the *Celebrity Pen* on the left hand side of the central reservation. The *meet and greet lady* performed her allotted task, and told me where to stand and wait as 9:48 approached, but until then I could wander around the area and chat to whoever I liked. I asked her the one remaining question in my mind,

"Who is actually interviewing me?" I asked, expecting that it would probably be one of their local team from Newcastle who I had never seen before.

"Hold on, let me check my running order" she said as she ran her finger down her clipboard.

"Right, Mike, you'll be interviewed by Jonathan Edwards."

"What – THE Jonathan Edwards?" I ask in star-struck amazement.

"Yes, we've only got one of him."

I think I just stood there in stunned silence while she dashed off in search of a crisis. I really did not know what to think, or do, at that moment. This was an Olympic Superstar, a sporting icon of the highest order, someone I had watched perform on the TV in awed respect for his world class talent. He had won an Olympic Gold Medal in 2000, and held the Olympic, World, European and Commonwealth Games titles all at the same time, and still held the world record for the Triple Jump. And this was the man who was going to be interviewing ME? This crazy day was just getting better and better!

Now there was just the small matter of how to fill the next half an hour. Basically I was stood in the middle of a motorway in Newcastle, dressed only in shorts and a flimsy running vest (well I couldn't be interviewed in a bin liner could I?), at half past nine on a Sunday morning, surrounded by celebrities and elite athletes. So the answer was simple. I wandered around the pen seeing who I could spot, and finding out which ones would speak to me and which ones wouldn't. Now I'm not an *autograph collector* by nature, and there's something strangely levelling about the fact that they too are stood there in the middle of the motorway, in flimsy running kit, not a minder or publicist in sight, with their *bits* freezing and as scared as any other runner about what they are about to undertake. I suppose the worst bit about it was that I found it extremely difficult to recognise anyone, partly because no one was used to seeing them like this, and partly because I never watch soaps, talent shows, reality shows, or read the tabloids. However I certainly did recognise Sir Chris Chattaway from across the pen, and had a few moments gossip with James Cracknell (it was clearly a good day for meeting Olympians) and Ben Fogle who were on a serious challenge to be the fastest celebrity.

Before I knew it, I was being lined up for my interview, with almost military precision, and it was obvious that the schedule they were working to meant that the only conversation I was going to get with Jonathan Edwards would be the live on camera one, as he was being moved around by a producer most unglamorously, with a cameraman in hot pursuit through the throng that was now building up. I was to be the second of two interviews done back to back in this corner of the pen, and in a flash we were live and the preceding interview was finishing already. The only things going through my mind were to look at him, rather than the camera, and REMEMBER TO SAY SOMETHING ABOUT PROSTATE CANCER – it was the charity that had given me the spot in the race, and this could be a good payback over and above the sponsorship money. Back home someone had set up the video recorder, so I could see it for myself in the context of the programme, but this also gave me the chance to make a transcript of the whole thing, which went exactly like this:

JE "Mike, let me come to you. You've lost even more in even less time."

ME "Yes, 2½ years ago I weighed 27½ stone. I'm now down to 12½"

JE "And what was the impetus for that?"

ME "I had a car accident, and thought that if I'm going to get another chance at this, then I'd better get it right."

JE "And who are you running for today?"

ME "I'm running for the Prostate Cancer Charity. When you consider that the same number of people running this race will actually contract prostate cancer this year I thought it's something I should do something about. I'd like to not have that happen next year."

JE "Well Good Luck Mike – and you look great!"

And with that he was gone, along with all the pressure, and the nervous excitement. The producer lady threw a "Nice interview, well done" over her shoulder as she swept away through the crowd, and I was free to get on with my day. It doesn't sound much put down in cold text like that, but it was fun, I had actually spoken with the man himself, and he had seemed like one of the good guys. More importantly, I had remembered to say what I had wanted to, which was an excellent performance under pressure as it is so easy to think you have far more time than you really do, and not get round to your own points in time. Most importantly, I found out later, The Prostate Cancer Charity people were delighted, as they had never got that sort of exposure at an event like this ever before, and had not expected that I would use the time to talk about them, rather than about me. I was also quite shocked later on that morning to find that people in the Newcastle area had actually really taken notice, as I heard two or three shouts running down through Jarrow congratulating me on the weight loss – utterly amazing, the power of TV!

Once I had gathered my thoughts, and had a gossip about the weight loss to a few TV soap stars who had been standing in close listening to the interview (and making sure they were seen on TV too), I realised that while I was leaning on the crash barrier doing some stretches, there were people on the other side doing exactly the same thing. The key fact here was that while the celebrities were in the front pen on the left of the central reservation, on the right was the elite start area. The few serious wheelchair racers were lining up for their early start ahead of everyone else just after 10:00, and behind them, just opposite me, were the Elite Women preparing for their start at 10:15. The lady doing her stretches about 10 feet away from me was none other than the incredible Paula Radcliffe herself, and as I whipped my camera out to save the moment for posterity she gave me a wonderful smile which I actually managed to capture. It made me realise properly, for the first time, the privilege that long distance running hands out to all who run these races. It is difficult to think of a single other sport of any nature, on any continent, where I would be welcomed to compete alongside, at the same time, in the same race, with World champions, Olympic champions, National champions, and where my name would appear on the same results sheet.

All the runners were by now assembled in the pens stretching way back up the motorway, and huge screens had been erected on the overhead gantries to keep the masses entertained. As soon as I had watched the wheelchair race start, and then the introductions of the top lady runners, and the start of their race, it was time for the *mass warm-up*. High up on a small stage set up above the runners waiting in the pen behind us was one of TV's keep fit gurus who would lead everyone through it. With his image being broadcast on huge screens above the runners into the distance back up the motorway the sight of 35,000 odd people being choreographed through their exercises and stretches was one to behold. Those numbers of people take up a lot of space, and with a gap between each of the pens from A to M they literally stretched out of sight. At the start gun each pen would be released one at a time, and the folks at the back, with the slowest predicted times could take three quarters of an hour just to get to the start line once the gun went. It was now that it finally dawned on the good folk in the celebrity pen that a few yards back behind our pen was Pen A, populated entirely by the fastest runners outside the elite athletes, and that when the gun was fired we were going to be inundated by a wall of fast runners eager to get on with it a lot faster than we wanted to. At that point I opted for discretion and worked my way quietly but purposefully through the (I wonder what the proper name for a *flock* of celebrities is – maybe a *pose* of celebrities?) crowd to the far left hand side of the pen, ready to hug the edge of the road and hopefully avoid the worst of the onslaught.

Sir Bobby Robson, himself a legend in most parts, but particularly in Newcastle, mounted the rostrum on the central reservation, fired the starting gun, and all hell broke loose as the Elite Male Athletes on the right hand side took off like bats out of hell, and one particular nutter from our side tried to outrun them before collapsing in a heap after about 500 yards. In seconds a tide of runners had engulfed me, and I just stuck to the barriers along the left of the road and soon found myself *high-fiving* the kids in the crowd of spectators lining the road.

The next 2 hours, 24 minutes and 11 seconds were a unique experience. The *oggies* in the motorway underpass; seeing my girls standing on the left of the Tyne Bridge (they had called to tell me they had arrived safely and where they were waiting to see me); the banter among the runners for the first few miles; the sudden quietness amongst the runners when we hit the long slow incline of the infamous John Reid Road; the Wall of Sound where one of the sponsors had set up huge speakers every few yards for half a mile to blast out favourite motivational songs; the unbelievably inspiring support of the locals who lined the route from start to finish, shouting your name read from your running vest, offering jelly babies and slices of fruit; the man standing on top of a bus shelter with a garden hose to cool you down just when it was getting too hot; the smell of the sea as you drop down the slope onto South Shields seafront with just a mile to go; the massed banks of supporters carrying you the final mile on their very own Wall of Sound; the sign 800 to go, then when you thought it would be 400 it was still *600 to go*; determination to run your best for that last stretch all the way to the finish; 200 to go and the final turn right, in towards the finish arch – *REMEMBER TO SMILE FOR THE CAMERA* – and crossing the finish Line.

Timing chip off, collect water and down half the bottle in one, collect MEDAL and T-Shirt. Stop and watch the Red Arrows doing their incredible display for US RUNNERS! Fight your way through the huge crowds to the tents of the Charity Village, and find The Prostate Cancer Charity Tent for an orgy of hugging and back-slapping with my four girls and the boys from Edinburgh. They really had brought a jar, but didn't seem too disappointed that they hadn't got to use it! The charity folk had laid on all the right drinks and refreshments for their runners, and it was great to meet up with some of the other runners on the Prostate Team and share the experiences of that incredible 13.1 miles.

As I stood outside the tent, with The Great North Run medal round my neck, a silver foil blanket round my shoulders, and having photos taken with my girls, it hadn't quite sunk in yet just how much that day had changed my life.

CHAPTER SIXTEEN

NIL BY MOUTH

I ROUNDED THE DAY OFF WITH A QUICK MEET UP WITH SOME OF THE OTHER bloggers running, and then headed for the coach back to my hotel for a shower and change. I had originally booked to stay over that night as I genuinely didn't know whether I would be up for a two hour train ride after the run, and had opted for the discretion of a good night's sleep over the valour of immediately attempting the long journey home. My support crew had gone straight back into Newcastle from South Shields in search of a suitable hostelry, and within a couple of hours I had hooked up again with them and set about properly re-hydrating (well that was my excuse and I was sticking to it!). We saw the girls off on their train back down south, and then managed to find an excellent Chinese restaurant where I felt perfectly fine forgetting my diet rules just this once. We then headed back to the station so that I could see the boys off on their trip back to Edinburgh. Their trip down had been by coach, as there was engineering work on the railway line, and we soon found that the trains were still not running and again there was a replacement coach service. The only problem was that the coach was now full, so the train company arranged to put them in a taxi, all the way back. Glad that my taxi ride would be considerably shorter, I was soon back at the hotel and finally got to bed. I set the alarm last thing before turning in, as I had to do a live interview over the phone with Hereward Radio back home at 7:00 in the morning, letting everyone know how I had got on.

I was actually wide awake when they phoned, and I had a really good interview with the morning show host Kev Lawrence. He was brilliant in one respect; he actually asked me if I had hit my sponsorship target, and gave me the chance to say that I was still a few hundred pounds short of my target. I failed to mention that I had kept putting up my target every time the total had approached it, and although my original target was £400, it was now *officially* £2000! Just after 9:00am I had a phone call from my local internet service providers, who had heard the interview, with a guarantee to make up the sponsorship to my target if it was still short at the end of the week. This is still the one and only time that any publicity has actually resulted in real sponsorship money – so well done and huge thanks to Cyberware!

Once that fun had died down, and I had managed a leisurely breakfast in the hotel dining room watching a few other very stiff-legged individuals negotiating their way around the tables, I was off to the station for the train home. It was packed solid, and I had a huge smile to myself to see that I was very, very far from being the only person on the train actually still wearing their medal around their neck for the journey home. The atmosphere on the train positively crackled with the almost deafening roar of unspoken respect between the runners, and I saw a number of people quietly fishing for their medals and slipping them on with a smile! Mind you, two hours of cramped conditions were not the perfect antidote for the legs the morning after, and my short walk home from the station was anything but smooth.

The surgeon had kindly scheduled the operation on my stomach skin for the 24th October, to give me time for a good break after the run to make sure I was fit for the table, so I now set about making the best of that break. In my usual inimitable style, I had managed to arrange a business meeting in Oxford on the Tuesday morning, so after one night off on Monday I had to face a day of driving cross country and back, without the benefit of motorways. I had a day with nothing special to do on the Wednesday, and on the Thursday I had an appointment to see Dr Ken and I made certain I had my medal with me when I went to the surgery. I think the object of that meeting was more for him to check everything was fine after the run, and before the operation, but I had nothing to worry about. He did try to get me to understand that the operation was quite a serious thing, but I was not listening to any talk of that nature – all I could see was the end product, and all they were doing was removing some loose skin, so as far as I was concerned it would all be a breeze and quite simple. It was not as though they were going to cut into muscle or anything like that, so there was no real point in worrying.

On the Friday, five days after the run, I was on a plane heading to Spain for the annual *Boys Week*. To be honest, the week didn't really start till the next Wednesday, but I had decided that I deserved a little extra, and as we were going to be staying at Duquesa, close to the Marina, I had organised to stay on the boat again for the few days before the rest of the boys arrived. I had a great few days just chilling out and recharging the batteries in the sun, and on the Wednesday I drove back up to the airport to drop off my little hire car and meet them in Arrivals at Malaga. At least this time they recognised me, as they were now quite familiar with the new look. By now we were sadly reduced to the position where we had no apartments in Spain between the entire FRA. Slacko had passed on a few short years ago, and The Hermit, who we had dropped in to see the previous year and persuaded to join us for the rest of that trip, had shrugged off his mortal coil a couple of months later. They are both sadly missed, and every time we meet up now the first drink is always to *Absent Friends*. The last apartment had now been sold, in order to acquire a place in Florida, so we were reduced to renting this year. However, when we finally arrived at the luxury, six bedroom apartment that we had hired through somebody one of the boys knew, we discovered that it was actually three medium-sized double beds! Now I know that we are all very good friends, and had been for years, but there is a line that has to be drawn in the sand in any relationship, and this was in grave danger of crossing that line. I immediately solved the problem as far as I was concerned, by deciding that as I had not yet packed my kit from the boat, I would continue to stay on it for the duration. I was completely comfortable there, and it was only a few yards from the local hostelries around the harbour, whereas the apartment was a good 10 minutes stagger. Auld Thai Tam also cottoned on to that key piece of information, and decided that he would join me on the boat (which easily slept four anyway), so the other three shared out the bedrooms and we headed for a bar.

We had a very relaxed time that week, took a few trips out in the boat, and generally did very little but wander around the place trying out new little local places, as we found them. The main topic of the week turned out to be deciding on the final nature of the order that they were going to place with my surgeon for a variety of *leather goods* just to make sure that the skin he was going to remove did not go to waste. In the end the consensus seemed to be for matching wallets for all the boys, although my personal misgivings seemed to carry very little weight in the discussions. As it happens, the surgeon wanted me to agree to let them have it for research purposes, and that appeared to be a much more satisfactory outcome for all concerned, but I'm not certain whether the boys ever forgave me. After another terrific week, rounded off with a beautiful day in bright sunshine on a sea as flat as millpond, when we took a pile of bread and cheese and a few bottles of wine and cruised up the coast past Marbella, it was time to go home.

In the few quiet moments I had during the holiday it had occurred to me that once the operation was done with I would need to think about some new goals. Everything had been about The Great North Run all that summer, and had given me a focus, but now there was no focus, no goal and no target. I had actually done something I had never ever thought possible; I had run a Half Marathon and lived to tell the tale. This, however, was over, and I would need something else. When I got back home, I was faced with a long tally of emails, and lots of them from the blog site. This was another thing I had not factored into the original equation of doing *a run* – the blog and the publicity and all the new friends. What was I going to do about that side of the *project* if I didn't do any more running? However, it was already becoming quite clear to me that I would keep up some sort of running, even if it was just for general fitness, as it was actually quite a fun pastime if you weren't pushing the training too hard. In fact, that feeling when I crossed the finish line at South Shields, and collected my medal, was like no other feeling I can ever remember having. The sense of personal achievement was overwhelming, not in a smug way, but in a quiet, life-affirming sense of inner strength and new found capability.

Then something inside my head latched on to the fact that I had done a half marathon, and asked the question that raised the bar:

"Since when is doing things by *half* good enough?"

This thought had settled into a corner of my mind, and was quietly festering away infecting all sorts of thought processes. It suddenly burst out of its corner with all guns blazing. In amongst the emails waiting for me to work my way through, was one from the Great Runs people offering me a guaranteed entry in the Edinburgh Marathon as a finisher at Newcastle. Yes, you guessed it, less than three weeks after doing my *one and only, never to be repeated* long charity run, I went ahead and paid for my entry into the Edinburgh Marathon taking place the following year on 25th May 2008. It was all done so quickly I hardly stopped to catch my breath and question the enormity of what I had just done. What on earth was I doing entering a marathon – it was only about six months or so away, and I was about to start that six months by having a big operation.

Now the operation was suddenly looming very large, and on the Tuesday I packed my bits and pieces according to the paperwork, and got the train down to Cambridge on the way to Addenbrookes Hospital. I had thought all along that the operation would be done in Peterborough, where all the clinics I had been to were held, but apparently the top team were based down there, and so that was where I would be sliced and diced. Mind you, when I arrived at Ward L5 I was thoroughly impressed, as it was in the new Addenbrookes Treatment Centre, a whole new wing not as yet officially *opened* by a visiting dignitary. The hospital here is the teaching hospital of Cambridge University, so a significant portion of this new wing was a research facility, but everything in the place was shiny and new, and the highest of high-tech.

For the rest of that evening I was subjected to a variety of tests to check that I was fit for the surgery the next day, and the first problem very quickly arose. They used these wonderful electronic gizmos for checking your heart rate and blood pressure, and although my BP was as fine as ever, my low heart rate immediately set off the automatic alarm on the kit. This took them by surprise, and led to various checks with my patient records, but it inevitably meant that I was immediately put down for an ECG before I could be allowed near a surgeon. I don't think I had my heart rate checked all the time I was in there without them having to turn off the beeper on the machine, but at least they soon got used to it and stopped worrying. I also had to go and have a medical photographer take some interesting shots of the skin they were going to remove, and as usual by now they were kind enough to say that they had never had to take photographs of anything quite like it before!

The day of the operation finally arrived. This meant nil by mouth from midnight. That's all very well, but it was no fun watching the other guys in the bay tuck into whatever was on offer. Then the surgeon came round to introduce himself to what he was taking on, have a good look, and draw all over me with a felt pen. Suddenly it was real, very bloody real, and the sizes of the lines he was drawing were literally breathtaking. He was a short guy, of African descent I think, but with a name quite difficult to pronounce so everyone called him *Deevor*. He had the most engaging smile and friendly way about him, which was just as well as he explained that he had never seen an operation of this type on quite this scale before – not a remark particularly designed to instil confidence!

Basically he drew a *fleur-de-lys* on me, with one *leaf* from my breast bone down virtually to my crutch, and the other two leaves going to each side along my waist, and right out to the extreme sides of my hips. It was HUGE! On a casual enquiry, he explained what he was going to do:

"Cut you open along these lines, remove everything between them and then pull the edges together and sew them up."

Holy shit, the guy was actually grinning! I tried to cling onto every word, as this was suddenly desperately serious – no longer some wonderful thing that was going to take the skin problem away, but this lovely guy was going to go for it with gusto, and a big sharp knife. He then told me that it was a fairly serious operation, and that I would be *out* on the table for probably over FOUR HOURS, making it dangerous and a little bit dodgy as once he had cut the middle bits out, there was no going back, and whatever happened they would just have to plough on.

"Oh, and we need you to sign this consent form, please, before we can proceed."

For one tiny moment... but I signed, he smiled again, and was gone with his piece of paper. I was left lying there, contemplating what he had said, and the lines on my stomach (and virtually everywhere else too). I also spent a little while doing something I had never really done before – contemplating my navel. It wasn't anything special, but I couldn't work out why I'd never done it before, as some would have us believe that it can be a mystic experience. I just lay there and contemplated it for old times sake really, and so that I could at least have a lingering memory of what it looked like, because by that night it would have ceased to exist, and therefore this was the last time in my life that I would ever be able to contemplate it. *It seemed only right and proper to actually do it that one time, just so I could genuinely say that once upon time I could, and so I did.*

And that was more or less how the rest of the time passed by that day, vague inconsequential ramblings passing the time, having a bit of banter with the nurses who looked in from time to time, and wondering when they were coming for me. I chose not to dwell on the operation, as by now I had been made starkly aware of the reality of it being major surgery, and the easiest way to cope with that was to ignore it completely. C'est la vie, que sera, sera! That's life, what will be, will be. Let's get this show on the road and then I can move on and get some new running shorts – funny what the mind comes up with to throw you of the scent when you're on the brink of something stressful.

Suddenly a porter arrived, and gave me two minutes to go to the loo. Dressed now in a surgical gown, flat out on the bed which had been unplugged from its own mechanical life support system, I was wheeled out of the ward to a chorus of good wishes from the nurses on duty. The porter, one of the nurses who had to accompany us and me on my bed filled the lift. It, and my spirits, sank a couple of floors, and then we headed along a long, quiet, white corridor towards the theatres. I'll never forget the experience of wheeling quietly along that long, bright white corridor which instantly conjured up the images recounted by people who have had *out of body or near-death* experiences. That was really not the type of thought I wanted at that moment for heaven's sake.

Once into the theatre area, I was handed over in some little ante room full of pumps and gauges and shelves full of packets of stuff. Someone introduced themselves as my anaesthetist, and started sticking needles into me and in next to no time I'm... back in the ward, trussed up like a Xmas Turkey with tubes with bags on the end emerging from deep inside dressings. Curtains round the bed; hushed voices; offers of water to sip through a straw. I'm offered some sort of button on a chord thing, which apparently if I press would make the pain diminish a bit. BP and heart rate checked every ten seconds, or at least it felt like it.

"Just let me sleep."

The next morning was still a bit hazy, but the highlight, if I can call it that, was the surgeon's round. It all got a bit crowded as I got the impression that my case had created a bit of a stir amongst the apprentice knife brigade (well, it is a teaching hospital). When I could get a word in edgeways I managed to enquire how much skin Deevor had actually removed, and was informed that he had taken off 3 kilos of skin. He was of the opinion at this stage that it had all gone rather well, even though it had taken him about five hours in the end. Unfortunately he was completely unable to tell me how many stitches I had received. This, of course, is one of the main pieces of information a patient requires after an operation, as it the one thing that will convey to your mates how big a deal it was, and how brave you were. Sadly he waved it away with a casual:

"Oh, a few hundred I should think – it's not worth trying to count them all, and most of them are below the surface anyway."

A FEW HUNDRED? How am I ever going to get away with a line like that? I'd have settled for 50 or 60, an impressive but believable figure which would raise eyebrows satisfactorily. But who was going to believe *a few hundred* – it was just too big! Then one of the other guys wanted a look at something amongst the dressings, and needed me to move slightly so that he could get at it. As my pillows and head were raised at the time, I just did a *plank* and raised myself in a straight line with just my shoulders on the raised head of the bed, and my heels lower down the bed. It's a great core strength exercise in the gym. Apparently I shouldn't have been able to do that in my condition, but as it was about the ONLY thing I could do I was more than happy to oblige. Mind you, it caused raised eyebrows all round! Then they checked on my medication, at which point someone had a bit of a go at the sister in charge about the fact that my *on demand* morphine pump wasn't working. They argued the toss for a bit about whether this thing was actually working or not, until I finally twigged what they were going on about – the button on a cord thing. When I joined in, they explained that it was obviously not working as the level had not dropped in the dispenser tube thing above my bed. It was supposed to give me a controlled level of morphine every time I pressed the button when the pain got too much, but as the level hadn't gone down, it was clearly not working.

"But I haven't pressed the button, so it's obviously not gone down. It's probably perfectly all right." said I, leaping to the nurse's defence. This caused a degree of scepticism.

"Why didn't someone explain it better to Mr Hare? He should have known how it works".

"I did know. I just didn't need any more pain relief. It seemed OK to me as long as I stayed fairly still, and someone gave me a tablet during the night sometime".

It was probably a simple case of where there's no sense there's no feeling, but I was never in any real pain as long as I stayed fairly still. But eventually I would have to move, for clinical reasons as much as for the obvious bodily ones. But what a rigmarole it was. Apart from the dressings basically covering just about everything from my neck to my thighs, I also had two *drains*. I didn't know a lot about these other than that they were tubes emerging from just above the top of my thighs on each side with little plastic bags on the end which collected a trickle of something with a distinctly unpleasant look about it in a deep shade of red. These little plastic bags lived in some flowery shoulder bags normally tied to the edge of the bed, but which had to be slung over the shoulder if I was to go anywhere. It took an average of about 10 minutes to cover the 5 yards to the loo and back, punctuated by sharp intakes of breath at certain key moments. Enough said!!

By the Friday afternoon, almost 48 hour after the operation, I was moving about a little more freely and even managed to sit out in my chair for my meals. This probably wasn't a good idea, as it clearly gave them just the excuse they were looking for, and ended with me being sent home at the weekend. The good news was a phone call from Number Four to tell me she was back safely from her school exchange visit to Delaware in the USA. She was currently Head Girl at her school, and so she had been required to give a talk at one of the school assemblies while she was there, and it had all worked out very well. She had also managed to visit Broadway during their little stop over in New York, and although they had not been able to fit in a show, just being there had been enough for the performer in her. Now while I was stunned at being turned out of the hospital quite so quickly, I was also delighted as it meant that I would actually be home on the Sunday for Number Four's 18th birthday. She had decided against having a party as soon as the opportunity for the trip to the US had come up, and had asked me to pay for the trip instead. I have long since learned not to argue about such things with the girls, so that was what she got. But now, against all expectation, I would at least be home with her for the actual day.

On Saturday morning it was confirmed that I would be discharged, and I was to arrange for someone to pick me up later on. They showed me how to change the dressings on my wounds, which I was now able to discover were actually a total of about 37 inches of stitches (on the surface), and gave me a supply of a variety of dressings, painkillers and antibiotics. The worst bit of all was the all-in-one Tubigrip corset – a sort of all round elastic support bandage which I had to wear to hold it all together until the stitches healed properly. One small spot on the stitches on my left side was still leaking something that looked quite nasty, but they said that it should dry up soon and all would be well.

The last act before getting the paperwork done was removing the drains. As far as I could tell, they were just there to drain out the bottom of the wounds, and probably didn't go in very far. So when the nurse undid the stitch holding the first one in place, and told me to take a deep breath and she would pull it out, I wasn't ready for what happened. The damn thing clearly went right to the top of the wound near my chest, and had obviously made itself quite at home over the three days. In fact it was distinctly unhappy about leaving – OH MY GOD that hurt... all the way down across the stomach and finally out by my thigh. It was agony for a minute or two. She repeated it with the drain on the other side, equally embedded, equally as far up the wounds, equally painful. I swear that was the most painful part of the whole show.

Once I'd packed, been handed my discharge paperwork, collected my bags of pills, potions and enormous dressings, and made my contribution with gratitude to the Ward Fund, I was pushed fraudulently to the front door in my wheelchair. I was perfectly capable of walking, but rules are rules. Finally I'm waved off to get on with it. Extremely glad to see the back of the place, however shiny and new and comfortable it was still a hospital, and no one can really say they enjoy being there. I was sooo glad to be home, although the three flights of stairs to the flat were a living nightmare for a very long few minutes. Decent food, decent telly, comfortable chairs and my own bed: everything I could possibly need to aid a speedy recovery. The rest of Saturday was a slow recovery from the *drains* trauma, but by Sunday I was feeling very much more relaxed, in myself. Although, it has to be said, I virtually needed a computer to work out how to take my pills. I had some that had to be *with food*, and some *on an empty stomach and others at least one hour before food*, which would have been easy if it wasn't for the fact that some were four times a day, and some were three times a day. It was a juggling act with an alarm clock to make it all fit in properly. It was not the most exciting of birthdays for Number Four, and I was in no condition to take her out for a meal, but she had a totally captive audience for her tales of her school trip to America, and the bonus was that I was home, which we had not really expected.

For the next couple of days I basically took it really easy, but the *leaky spot* in my dressings meant that I was having to change that bit on a daily basis, even though it was best to leave the dressings alone as much as possible. By the Monday I actually ventured out for a coffee, but it was still a little bit awkward getting back up the stairs, especially with the *corset thing* still restricting movement to an extent. On the Tuesday the leaking was getting a little dodgy, and I was starting to see the time coming when I would run out of dressings, if I kept going through them at this rate. I decided to wander gingerly round to the local NHS Drop-in Centre and get them to give me a decent opinion. In retrospect, this was not as good an idea as it first seemed, as this sort of thing was way outside their comfort zone, but they did their best. They took a swab of the *ooze*, and patched up the dressings for me with the advice to come back if it continued.

On the Wednesday it had got a little worse, and by now the corset was developing a nasty stain too from the leak, and this was going to present a whole new problem. So I visited the drop-in centre a second time, and this time they got straight on the phone to the ward at Addenbrookes for an opinion from the duty doctor. This resulted in the request that I *pop down* so that they could take a look and dress it properly once again, so I grabbed some cash and meandered slowly to the station to get the next train down to Cambridge. On arrival at L5 I was laid out on a handy bed for the *once-over*, and immediately informed that I was not going home that night.

"But I haven't got any kit with me" I feebly protested, to absolutely no avail.

"Get someone to pop some down for you."

"Yeah, sure! The only daughter with a car lives 15 miles further away than my place, and she works till 8 o'clock at night! She's probably 60 miles away!"

"Well sort something out tomorrow, you're going nowhere with that infection."

Oh great! So the wound was infected. They enquired as to when it had started to behave like that, and I pointedly responded that it had, in fact, been exactly like that BEFORE I had been discharged! Anyway, I was written up for *broad spectrum* antibiotics, meaning that they hadn't a clue what the infection was till they got the lab results, so they were going to hit me with everything to cover all bases in the meantime. So there I was, stuck back in hospital, 40 odd miles away from home with just what I had been stood up in when I was sent there. One phone call and a request to pass the word around was enough to get everyone worked up at home, so I spent the evening trying to reassure the girls that everything was really OK and that it was *just routine*. Obviously it wasn't, but I didn't want the girls throwing a wobbly at that distance. Number Three duly arrived later on the next day with a few bits and pieces from home to keep me going, and I spent the next couple of days popping pills and lying around with a fair degree of frustration while a succession of nurses came by and changed the dressings on a regular basis. The one real bonus was that I didn't have to wear the corset while I was in a hospital bed.

Within a couple of days the decision was taken finally to put me on to the *good stuff* – intravenous antibiotics. Obviously this was a fair indication that progress was NOT being made as desired, and it had the undesirable side effect of hooking me up to a bag stand on wheels. This development severely restricted my mobility, and brought an abrupt end to my little trips to the circle of shops and coffee bars in the centre of the hospital where I could get a paper and a decent coffee each morning. I also started to form the impression that things were not quite going to the plan that the *doctor had ordered*, prompted by the increasing number of checks, and the repetition of swabs being taken for analysis.

I was also becoming heartily sick of the *food* in there. It might have been a fabulous new facility, with all the latest high-tech gizmos going, but the food was utterly diabolical. By now, of course, I had developed an acute sense of what was good food, and what was bad. I had also been able to check out carefully what the NHS was keen to tell everyone was good food and what was bad. My problem was, that whilst the NHS publicity machine was stridently telling everyone what was good for them, the hospital was merrily serving up an unadulterated diet of all the bad stuff to their inmates. Could I get a high fibre breakfast with low sugar content? NO! Could I get a wholemeal sandwich at lunchtime? NO! I actually ended up with my own packet of breakfast cereal in my locker, and resorted to salads for main meals – no fun in November.

By now I was getting more than a little hacked off at the lack of either progress or information as to what the problem was. On the plus side, the other guys in the bay had finally got the information out of me about my weight loss project, and had been on the internet and looked at the website. I was now on excellent first name terms with the nursing staff on the ward, and they had also been looking at the website, and checked back through my notes, so I was now being introduced to visitors as The Incredible Shrinking Man! By the weekend I noticed that the top guys on the team were now dropping by to check me over, which I did not take as a good sign, so I thought it was about time I started demanding some answers. The ones I got were not what I had hoped for, as it turned out that they had not been able to identify whatever the bug was, as by the time the ooze got to the surface the antibiotics had killed it off rendering the swabs useless. However it was still beavering away inside, whatever it was. They also started talking about *necrosis*, which turned out to be some sort of breakdown of the tissues where they were supposed to binding back together. It was then that the penny finally dropped about just how serious this operation had really been, and that the process was very far from being completed.

But now the powers that be decided that slightly more drastic action was required, and they would *relieve* the wound around the leak. That sounded like perfectly good sense to me, but I was distinctly unprepared for what happened next. As soon as the treatment room off the side of the ward was free, I was wheeled in there and placed myself carefully on the treatment table while the young duty doctor performed his ritual ablutions.

"This might hurt a bit."

The translation from *Doctorese to plain English* goes roughly like this: "*Prepare to meet thy doom! Try not to wake up the patients having their afternoon sleep with your childish screaming! The pain will probably ease off after three days!*"

What he actually did was to lie me down, and brutally hack through the stitches holding me together at that point. He *relieved* about four inches of the wound, without ANY anaesthetic or warning at all, and then just let the wound *peel open* at that point. He swabbed it down, and pronounced that it had been a good job! How on earth I kept my mouth shut I have no idea, but it had been absolutely excruciating agony for a minute or two, and now I was left with a stretch of open wound. I was duly returned to my bay to wait for the cold sweat to dry.

Shortly after, the charge nurse on duty that afternoon, a great guy called Steve, wandered by for a chat, and enquired as to whether the anaesthetic was wearing off yet. I queried that fairly frankly, and on checking the notes he remarked:

"Oh, he didn't use any!" accompanied by his eyebrows giving an excellent impression of an express lift in *up* mode. To his eternal credit he immediately departed to make me a good strong mug of coffee.

However, even with bits hanging out of big new gaping holes, and antibiotics pumping into my veins like Chardonnay at a Wags Ball, no discernable improvement transpired, so they started to discuss alternative approaches. By the Wednesday, a week after I had been summarily re-admitted, and by which time I was ready to explode with the frustration and going rapidly stir-crazy, they opted for the drastic approach. They made the decision to take me back into theatre, open up the whole wound again and give it a right good scouring out with carbolic and wire wool (or the clinical version of that approach). Then they would introduce some magic new piece of equipment they had which would be left inside the wound when they closed it up again, attached to some sort of electronic pump on the outside. There was no way of knowing how long this would all have to be in place, but it was now their *best shot* at sorting this out. I was scheduled for the next morning, and returned to the *nil by mouth* list. Oh joy – no more hospital food for a day!

The next morning I was gowned and prepped for theatre, and a large suitcase was placed on the bed beside me with instructions to guard this with my life. It was the aforementioned *magic new piece of equipment*, and was worth more than its weight in gold. Off we duly went, on the same route through lifts, the blinding white *near death* corridor, and into the theatre complex. Same old same old – tubes and needles and things before instant oblivion, but I was just about past caring before I passed out anyway.

Coming round slowly on the ward later on was a lot more comfortable than I expected, and I was surprised to find that I had a very nice neat dressing in place and not a single tube sticking out anywhere, not even one of those subversively nasty drains in a cute little shoulder bag. There was no sign of anything resembling *a magic new bit of equipment* hooked up anywhere either. Steve had no idea what was going on, but told me that Deevor would be round when he finished his theatre list to tell me the outcome. I had a drink and a bite to eat, and before long he showed up with his trademark grin in full flower. He had opened up the wound completely, washed it all out, and found that the antibiotics had obviously done the trick and everything was now settled down and as it should have been originally. The decision had been made that nothing further was required, so the equipment had not been installed and he had just sewed me back up neatly and tidily and that should be an end to it. He was delighted with the final outcome, so I decided that I should be as well. The funniest part was when they realised that their wonderful new piece of kit had not only not been attached, but had not been returned with me either, and a search party was immediately despatched to scour the area to find it before it disappeared into some NHS black hole.

I was to be kept in another day, just to make sure there was no reaction to the latest surgery, and by the Friday night they were satisfied that I was in order, so arrangements were made to discharge me again on the Saturday. So I finally got out of there by the Saturday afternoon, with fairly explicit instructions from the nurses, in the nicest possible way, not to come back again. I was feeling a lot better by now than when I had come home the first time, and had formed the definite opinion that although they had probably been way too keen to discharge me the first time, this time I really was going to be fine. I was still trussed up in that damnable corset, and was under strict instructions that I had to wear it for at least six weeks, and I had a bag of spare dressings and a collection of five different pills to take. My discharge letter said that the reason for admission had been *emergency other source* and the diagnosis was suitably vague as *post-abdominoplasty wound infection or fat necrosis*. I would have to attend the dressings clinic the next week, and come back to see the surgical team in a fortnight, but that was me out of there finally on the 10th November.

It was probably just as well that I had gone into the whole surgery thing with my eyes effectively tightly closed. If I had ever really understood just what major surgery it was, and the possible outcomes, I might never have gone ahead with it. Instead I had chosen to focus entirely on the fact that they would simply remove the skin overhang, and I would toddle back out a new man, without ever thinking what that actually entailed. In the end I *had* actually toddled back out a new man, but until the dressings and corset were off I wouldn't really appreciate it properly. However the surgery had left more than my torso scarred.

CHAPTER SEVENTEEN

'INSPIRATIONAL AMBASSADOR'

THERE IS A STRANGE *LAW* IN SCIENTIFIC CIRCLES – THE LAW OF UNINTENDED Consequences. It basically means that whenever you do something new or different, it will somehow cause something to happen which you were completely and utterly unaware would be a consequence. In the case of my surgery, there was indeed a *complication* resulting from the operation. In my blog I referred to it as ITS – Insecure Trouser Syndrome. I found myself for a while, in a very strange position, as I couldn't use a belt or drawstring, on my trousers because of the long line of stitches stretching right across my waist from hip to hip. There was no way of actually buying anything elasticated, as I still had absolutely no idea whatsoever of what my waist measurement would actually be, until I had the dressings finally removed. So for a while I was reduced to some strange solutions, the most novel being in the end deciding to use safety pins to attach some light jogging bottoms to the corset thingy.

I hated that Tubigrip elastic thing with a vengeance, and experimented with a Velcro waist support about a foot deep, which I had originally bought when trying to find a way of holding the loose skin under control for running. It turned out to be the perfect solution, but not really deep enough, so I quickly acquired another three, so that I could use two at a time, one above the other to cover the wound completely, and have a set to wear while one was in the wash. Totally practical, extremely comfortable, and luxuriously adjustable unlike the elastic rubbish one from the hospital. In fact when I attended the dressing clinic a week later the sister in charge said that she had never seen anything like it, and would be recommending it to anyone who needed something like the corset thing as it was the best thing for the job she had ever seen.

Another week later and I was back at the hospital for my post-operation check with the boss Mr Malata, who decided that everything was now very much in order and going according to plan. In fact his actual words were "Spectacularly successful surgery" and "brilliant progress and recovery". I was allowed to do without the *corset* at night, but still had to wear it during the day for a few more weeks, and I was allowed to drive again. I explained that I needed to know when I could get back into training, as I had a marathon to do in May in Edinburgh, and his first reaction was to refer me for psychological evaluation, but then he said he thought it was typical of me, and wished me luck. He agreed that I could try some light work sessions on a treadmill, but that I should be very careful and feel my way back gently, listening for any sign of complaint from my body. The appointment was at 15:30, and by 17:30 I was on the treadmill at the gym, (in my corset), for a gentle 2 mile trial run.

Plans at this point got extremely complicated. Whilst having a chat a few weeks previously with the girls from The Prostate Cancer Charity I had mentioned that I would be doing the Edinburgh Marathon for them in May. They had asked me why I had chosen to do Edinburgh and not London, and I had explained that, even though it's every runners dream to do the London Marathon, it was too late to get a place other than a Bond Place with them, and that I could not commit to raising the £2000 pounds to guarantee a bond place anyway. Since then they had clearly had some internal discussions, and as a result of the large sum I had raised for them through The Great North Run, but particularly because of the incredible publicity I had got for them, they decided to give me a place anyway, without any fund raising commitment at all. This was totally unheard of, and an offer I couldn't possibly refuse – I might never get another chance to run London as long as I was running. So now I had the awful knowledge that here I was in December, trussed up in my corsets, stitched together like a patchwork quilt, but on 13th April I was intending to run The Flora London Marathon, followed by the Edinburgh Marathon on 25th May for good measure. A normal training plan for a marathon I was assured took at least 16 to 20 weeks, but here I had only 17 weeks, and the first 4 of those would be in a corset, with 37 inches of stitches trying to knit together properly.

Maybe Mr Malata had been right in the first place. Maybe I DID need psychological evaluation.

To take my mind off all this, I had to find my way to Edinburgh for the annual Xmas lunch of the FRA on the 18th December, where the news of my impending marathon exploits was greeted with a sort of resigned incredulity. After the debacle of the replacement coaches on their trip to watch me at Newcastle, they instantly opted to concentrate their efforts on the Edinburgh Marathon, rather than even think about London. It was the blindingly obvious approach anyway, and part of the reason that I had entered the Edinburgh one in the first place. I'm sure if it had been somewhere completely different I would probably not have given it a second thought when the email came through. After the previous year's disappointment with the change of ownership of our normal haunt for these lunches, we were trying out a new location – The Mussel and Steak House in The Grassmarket just below the castle. Although they didn't have a *Xmas Menu* available, we had a terrific meal and probably overstayed our welcome by a large margin, not that they would ever have told us that. The bottom line was that it received sufficient approval for a repeat booking to be made for the next year.

Xmas was spent at home at the flat, with the girls all coming round, with current victims in tow, to do the cooking. We had a great day, and got through the usual routine of Star Wars Monopoly and a very late night of Texas Hold 'em accompanied by a variety of liquid refreshments. The girls had, of course, decided that they were all coming to London for The Marathon, and so they took the chance while they were all together to cook up their plans. I was still restricting myself to the treadmill at this stage, but had also begun to sneak in some core exercises on my abs and mid-section, partly because they are excellent for running, but also just to see if I could do them without doing any damage.

By the beginning of January 2008 I felt ready to try a run outside, but the weather was not very kind, so I stuck to the gym and added a few more of the core sessions. I now felt that enough time had passed, so ditched the corset, and went shopping. This was one hell of an ego boost, as I could finally find out what my waist really was now after the surgery had removed the last vestiges of the old stomach. At my worst I had a waist of 61 inches, but now it was a staggering 38 inches! I had gone down 23 inches on my waist, and I was once again able to buy clothes on the High Street everywhere. In any shop, if I saw something I fancied I actually knew it would fit. Until you have been there and done it, it is virtually impossible to know what an intense feeling of pleasure and satisfaction this simple thing can bring. After years of not being able to shop for clothes, that easy step was a deep psychological joy. I did not go mad, as I would take my time and just get stuff as the need arose specifically, but knowing that I could just nip out and buy something was a totally new experience.

I also knew that I should be looking around for a warm-up race to get back into the swing in the run up to the London Marathon. The classic idea was to do a half-marathon in early March, and the usual one for our area was the Silverstone Half, which took place on the track at Silverstone motor racing circuit. For some reason I didn't fancy that race, probably because I had seen some reports about it being a bit boring and windswept which were obviously just the views of a couple of runners out of many thousands, but I avoided it anyway. I spotted another one, just a bit earlier on the 24th February at Sleaford which wasn't too far from home, so I duly entered as my first race of 2008.

Now, I was talking about the Law of Unintended Consequences before, and suddenly I was faced with another complete surprise – two of my girls, and their respective boyfriends, had decided that they would like to have a go at doing The Great North Run with me this year. Now it would be perfectly fair to say that none of them had ever done any running like this before, but basically they had been inspired by watching the run in a very *up close and personal way*, and really wanted be part of something like that. This was completely out of the blue for me, and whilst I expected that Number Four would go through with it, as would Number Three's boyfriend, I was less certain about the others. Number Three had suffered from knee and ankle problems as she grew up, and had required surgery on her ankle at one stage. In the light of this I was fairly confident that such a distance run would be beyond the capabilities of that ankle, but I promised to support her all the way, and even got a sports physiotherapist to take a look and give her some advice about training on it. The same applied to Number Four's boyfriend, in a different way. He had been a promising young footballer in South

Wales until a bad injury had required knee surgery and put him out of the game permanently, so again I offered support but without expectation. They all put their names into the ballots for places, and we waited to see the outcome.

The Edinburgh Marathon people were by now sending out regular email newsletters and had well over 10,000 runners registered, so it was going to be a good event. The latest newsletter had requested *interesting stories* so I had sent off a reply with a few details, and they had come back showing keen interest and asking for a few more details. When I got the next one on the 22nd I was casually reading through when I suddenly realised I was looking at pictures of me. They had put a whole section in on my story with some pictures they had got from my website, and were extremely complimentary, which was a great boost for the training I was putting in now. This was all going very well, and I was enjoying the running more than ever. I had even bought myself some running tights for the cold weather, but carefully avoided any pictures for a while. A day or so after the piece in the Edinburgh newsletter I had a phone call from a lady at the Scottish edition of *The Sun* newspaper, wanting to do an interview for an article, so I chatted to her for a while but she wasn't sure when it would appear. On the 31st I noticed an interesting article on the BBC News website about the use of anti-obesity drugs, and as they asked for comments, I duly made some. I was quite shocked to get a phone call later that morning from one of their journalists wanting to chat about my comments. The upshot of that conversation was that they sent a car to pick me up that afternoon to take me to their Cambridge studio and before I knew it I was doing a live interview on the BBC News that evening. The fascinating thing here was that they were not intrinsically doing an interview about what I had done, but were genuinely seeking my opinions about this breaking news story. This was a whole new departure, and I must admit that I enjoyed the experience immensely, and they were again complimentary about the interview. While I was sitting around waiting for the interview, I got chatting to the BBC Look East lady who was operating the camera for the London end, where the main News Presenter would be doing the actual interview over the live link. When we had finished, she asked if it would be OK to give me a buzz sometime, for their own local programme, and of course I said "Yes" and thought nothing more of it.

In true *never a day goes by* style, I was then told that a double page spread on me running the local marathon was being published in The Sun in Scotland that Saturday, and they were kind enough to send me a copy. It was a typical Sun style article, but nowhere near as bad as I had feared. In fact their sub-headline announcing the fact that I had shed *the equivalent of 44 big bags of spuds* brought a wry smile to my lips, not only because it was so graphically accurate, but also as it was such a clever connection to the main sponsors of the Edinburgh Marathon – the huge Scottish potato producers Albert Bartlett. Almost before I had got over that one, the lady from BBC Cambridge really did phone me, wanting to arrange to record a short profile film on me for their main evening programme on the 4th February. We ended up in the local country park where I did all my training, as the crew who came out thought that there were some very photogenic spots to use as back-drops. They asked if I would come to meet them there in my running kit, so that they could get a few shots of me running in the park, so I duly obliged. It was all very well doing repeated short runs alongside the lake till they got it right, but then they wanted to set up the camera on the back of their truck and film me running along immediately behind it pretending that it wasn't there. Next they wanted to repeat this, but with the truck driving along beside me to get some good side-on footage. I covered over 3 miles while they got *a few shots* of me running, and of course most of it never saw the screen. However they did put together a terrific little profile film which went out on BBC Look East that night.

Once that crazy couple of weeks was over, I could get back to preparing properly for my approaching runs, and by coincidence received an appointment to see the surgical team again on the 25th February, the day after the Sleaford Half Marathon. This was excellent timing, as at least it would be too late for them to stop me doing that run. I also suddenly realised that there had been another dramatic change in my life without me properly recognising it. The whole of the previous year had been totally focussed on the attempt to do something amazing – The Great North Run. Something so immense it had surprised everyone I knew, including myself. Now suddenly, without clearly thinking about it, I was about to run another half marathon, within 3½ months of the last operation, just as a training run. Had I quietly slipped through a time warp into a parallel universe while I was on the operating table? I checked back on my training stats from my Garmin and realised that on my training run on the 2nd February, only my the third run outside since the operation, I had actually run farther than the Great North Run, and that I had passed the half marathon distance 20 seconds faster than I had done the distance in Newcastle. I think at that point it was fair to conclude that I was pretty well recovered from the operation, and that training was going well.

By the 24th I was good and ready for a decent run, and drove up to RAF Cranwell, near Sleaford, where the run was based. It was one of those rare events which turned out to be a bit cliquey and elitist, but what the hell, I was there now, they had taken my entry fee and I was going to run whether anyone would speak to me or not. The race was due to start just across the playing fields from the main stand, go across the sports field and out onto the roads away from the base, eventually returning to finish in front of the stand. There was also to be a 5k Fun Run after the main race had started, which would be based on some long loops within the playing fields. When the main race started the runners all followed the lead car with the timing clock on its roof, and we ran across the field, then round a large loop back past the start and then out across the field onto the roads and away. I spent the first half of the race wondering why *Dippi* (my Garmin) was giving me a completely different distance totally at odds with each of the mile markers, till it eventually dawned on me that the classically elitist organisers of the race had completely cocked up beyond belief. The loop round the field and back past the starting line was obviously a horrendous mistake – the driver of the lead car had clearly got himself totally confused and taken us round the first loop of the fun run course, adding a significant chunk to the race distance! The penny finally dropped for me when I realised that the mile markers were wrong by the distance I had checked when we crossed the start line once again. This would either mean that we were going to have to run a fair bit further than a half marathon, or that the organisers would be currently buzzing around like the proverbial *blue-arsed flies* desperately trying to measure a new finishing point some distance from the planned finish line. The latter proved to be the case, as we were suddenly shouted at by marshals as we ran past them telling us that the finish line had been moved.

I didn't enjoy the race much, especially not the two miles *off road* on frozen, rutted, motorcycle tyre-gouged tracks through fields, and it was quite a lonely run amongst the stragglers near the back of the field, but I actually finished in 2 hours 18 minutes 27 seconds and came 285th out of 304 finishers. This was fully 5½ minutes faster than my Great North Run time, and therefore my Personal Best time for a half marathon. The long cold trudge back across the field for another mile to get back to the changing rooms was extremely unpleasant, and the walk was punctuated by loud complaints from many other runners. Although the organisers must have been hugely embarrassed by their overt demonstration of total incompetence, no matter how many times I checked their website I never saw them post an apology up to the runners. Needless to say this one was NOT placed in the *must do again* column of life's little shopping list!

Next day was the appointment with the surgeon again, but when I turned up I was introduced to a new slightly younger consultant surgeon who would be seeing me, Mr Gillespie. He had a bit of a poke around, took the blood pressure and heart rate again, and then said that he had noticed from my notes that I had done the Great North Run. He then offered me the good news that I would probably be fine to start running outside again now, if I felt up to it. When I couldn't stop myself from bursting out laughing, he looked perplexed, so I explained that I had just got a PB in the Sleaford Half yesterday. Once he had digested that fact, and readjusted his thinking about how well I was doing, we got into a conversation about running as he was a runner too and had done one or two marathons himself. He then switched back to clinical matters, and told me that he was the guy who would be doing my thigh surgery in due course. I had almost forgotten about that for the moment, but he explained exactly what he was intending to do. I asked him about when he would put me on the list, and he said immediately, which would probably mean doing the operation in about eight weeks or so.

At this point I asked if I could influence the timing at all, and explained my plans for the London and Edinburgh Marathons in April and May. At first he couldn't believe that I was intending to do a marathon so soon after the abdominal operation and then refused to believe that I was intending to run two marathons in six weeks. Once we had established my racing programme, and that I was also going to do the Great North Run again at the beginning of October, he asked me if it would be convenient to do the operation just after Edinburgh. He reasoned that doing it then should give me enough time to recover for Newcastle, so I agreed and he made the entry in his diary list. I must admit that this co-operation was so far away from my expectation of the NHS, but nevertheless I knew perfectly well how lucky I was, and well aware of how grateful I should be.

As life drifted into March, I was thinking it was about time that I had a quiet few weeks in order to get myself ready for my first marathon, and hopefully without too much extra stuff going on. It seemed as though my wish would be granted, and a couple of weeks drifted past punctuated by some very effective training runs round the park. On the 6th I realised that it was now exactly a year since I started my blog on the Realbuzz site, which had by now become almost a daily routine. I had a look back at some of my early posts and could hardly believe the progress I had made. I also took a note of the statistics showing on the blog, which revealed that my idle ramblings on there had received 163,358 visits, and 1,802 comments had been left by visitors in that time. Although it had taken some time for the traffic to build up as people got to know me, the blog had now reached the stage where it was attracting about 400 visits every day.

Then I got a call from Sam, the lady that owned and ran the local running shop where I get my running shoes and most of my kit, Advance Performance. We had often chatted over the last year, and she was very well aware of my story – she had even put a little piece in one of her shop's newsletters which went out to all her online customers as well as callers at the shop. She wanted to introduce me to someone and have a chat about The Great Eastern Run, the local annual half marathon in Peterborough, if I was free to join them for a coffee one morning. Intrigued to find out what Sam was up to, I agreed and immediately went on to the internet to see what I could find out about this race, and try to work out why I had never come across it, or seen it happening. It turned out to be quite a large event organised by the city council, with over 2,000 runners the previous year, and took place around the centre of the city, starting and finishing at points within a couple of hundred yards of home. The reason I had not come across it at all was that it always took place in early October, when I was historically away in Spain with the boys, and of course in previous years there is no way I would ever have been interested in running. This year it was scheduled to be held on the 12th October, exactly one week after The Great North Run, so I went for that coffee and chat at least with some basic knowledge so I wouldn't look a complete idiot.

It transpired that the someone to whom she wanted to introduce me was the Assistant Race Director from the Council, and after a chat about my story they explained that they would like to ask me to become the *Official Inspirational Ambassador* for the Great Eastern Run. You've got to love the sound of that title, but I had no idea of what this would mean in terms of time and effort on my part, although it would clearly mean something was required. Basically we could work out what the role was as we went along, but they wanted to put some details of my story on the Race Literature, and a page about me on the website for the race. Also I would perhaps do some local radio interviews, and turn up on the promotional stand that they put up in the local shopping centres three or four times during the summer. It also, of course, meant doing the run, and as I had already confirmed my Great North Run entry it would mean doing two half marathons on back to back Sundays. Once I remembered that my main weekly long runs on Sundays in my build up to London were well over that distance anyway, I agreed to go ahead, but on one condition. My terms for taking on the role, and letting them use the story to hopefully inspire other local people to take part, were that The Prostate Cancer Charity should be made one of the main charities associated with the race, and that they should have a free stand at the little promotional exhibitions and a free spot on the field at the end of the race itself. All this was readily agreed, but nothing was to be announced until they had got the new printing done, prepared the necessary press releases, and had the idea finally signed off by the main race director. At times like this I would wonder whether Dr Ken had the slightest idea of what he was unleashing with his little *running idea* a year or so ago.

Apart from this interesting little development, March remained blissfully quiet, and my training went according to plan. I even took a notable diversion one Sunday morning at the end of the month to pop out to do the Thorney Road Runners 10k Race, just for a change and to support a great little local running club which had the knack of putting on some excellent races and being extremely welcoming to stray *private runners* like me. It was a glorious spring morning and somewhere near 300 runners turned out from all around the area. I was not intending to bust a gut here, just try to put in a good time without disturbing or damaging any part of the *organism* only two weeks before London. As so often happens when you take that attitude I was going extremely well as I passed the 8k marker, with a Personal Best for the distance clearly up for grabs. As I try to do in every single race, I was now starting to overtake those people who had gone off too fast in the first half of the race, using the backs of runners ahead as targets to overhaul. I had been tracking one particular big guy who was starting to slow down a bit as we neared the 9k mark, and as I passed him he stopped dead in his tracks. I called out:

"You OK, mate?"

And he responded with a gasped:

"It's my first race, and I'm not even going to finish it."

Without thinking, my immediate retort was:

"Sod that! Of course you are – we'll do it together"

I handed him the remains of the drink I had been carrying, abandoned the idea of a PB, and proceeded to encourage and goad him towards the finish line. To my mind that is what running is all about once you get a little way back in the field with those who are not there to win, but just to take part. It is about a shared experience and exploring the art of the possible, and I just wanted him to achieve his goal of doing that race. If I had left him there, he might never have entered another event, even hung up his running shoes for good so as not to experience that failure again. As it was, he had no idea who I was, and all he would remember in the future is that he did the race, and finished in front of his family crossing the finish line with a huge grin on his face to a large round of applause. It was a sensational way to spend a Sunday morning, and I drifted back to my gym afterwards for a well earned session in the steam room and Jacuzzi, contemplating upon how terrific life could be just when you weren't expecting it.

But now it was April, with the Flora London Marathon looming very large (and very long) on the 13th. I had just found out that by one of those strange quirks of fate I had landed upon a very special running of the race. It was going to be the 100th Anniversary of the London Olympics Marathon of 1908, which was the first time that the *Marathon Race* had been run over the precise distance of 26 miles 385 yards. Since then that exact measurement has become the officially recognised standard distance for all Marathons the world over, so the medals this year would be special commemorative medals for "*1908–2008 100 years of the distance*". How cool was that!

This was one of those races where you had to go to a special Expo in the few days before the race to collect your Race Pack (bib number, timing chip etc). The Expo was down at an exhibition centre in London Docklands for the four days from Wednesday to Saturday, and I applied some logic to determine that the least busy day would be the Thursday, on the basis that the excitement for London-based runners would get them there on the Wednesday, and that any runners having to travel and stay in London would not arrive before the Friday at the earliest. So on the Thursday I headed off down to London and across on the Docklands Light Railway to the Expo, where the queues were very light, with only one person ahead of me in my number block for the race packs. Nice to know you can get some things right. However, on that subject I had booked an overnight stay on the Saturday night, just to be on the safe side, with a package which included a pasta meal on the Saturday night and transport to the race start by coach on the Sunday morning. When I arrived at the Expo I had a bit of a look round on the way to it from the DLR station, and spotted that my hotel was right opposite the centre there, and quickly realised that as I was going to be checking in there on Saturday afternoon I could actually have saved myself the bother of today's trip. So nice to know that you can also get things horribly wrong at the same time as well!

As I wandered around the Expo, I collected all the free bits and pieces being handed out by the various stalls; some good, some not worth having. Then I took off my jacket to change my appearance, and reversed my direction to go back round and see if I could blag any more of the good bits and pieces, as you do at these things. Suddenly I spotted a stall which immediately drew my attention, and I headed across to pick up some literature and have a chat with the Greek lady on duty there. There were a lot of stalls advertising great marathon races around the world, but this one particularly took my eye. Ever since becoming involved in the world of marathons and half-marathons I had taken the trouble to find out what I could about what lay behind this famous race distance, and the legend of the run by the messenger Phidippides, from Marathon to Athens. He was instructed by the Greek general to take the news to Athens of the small Greek Army's defeat of the massive invading Persian Army at the Battle of Marathon in 490 BC, and he had run all the way, passed on the message and then fallen down dead on the spot. This stall was advertising The Athens Classic Marathon, the one and only *authentic Marathon*, re-tracing the route Phidippides ran from Marathon to Athens, with a finish in the original Olympic Stadium. I had absolutely no idea that this race existed, but I was instantaneously hooked. I knew that whether I finished London or not, whether I finished Edinburgh or not, however many times I ran races that were *marathons*, I could never truly and honestly call myself a marathon runner in my heart of hearts until I had run THE MARATHON! I did have the presence of mind to take the details and not actually enter the race, which was scheduled for the 11th November. Let's face it; I hadn't even tried to run *any* marathon yet. I had two coming up, and then I was facing surgery on my thighs in June, so this was absolutely no time to be entering another marathon in November. But I knew it was going to have to be done one year. In that flash of seeing the stall and realising what it was advertising, I had acquired a new long term target. But now it was time to stop dreaming and get organised, I had a race on Sunday!

CHAPTER EIGHTEEN

THE SPRING DOUBLE

I AM ON THE EDGE OF TOTAL EXHAUSTION; COLD TO THE MARROW YET dripping with sweat; it has gone deathly quiet, and I am running slowly down a long dark tunnel. No, not completely dark, just a shimmering dull orange glow – orange stripes above me along the ceiling, ranks of orange blobs down both sides of this orange tunnel. What am I running on? It's not a road, it's a surface of orange glue which is trying to grab my feet, which only just escape from its clutches at each faltering step with a faint squelch which becomes louder and louder to banish the deafening silence of the tunnel. Heavy breathing around me, others squelch through the tunnel at my side, glazed eyes focussed unwaveringly ahead.

Is there a light ahead?

Will this silence ever be broken again?

How much more glue will there be spread across this road?

It's funny how the mind works sometimes, but that little episode is one of my clearest and most lasting memories of the 2008 Flora London Marathon. The experience had started with the train down to London on the Saturday afternoon, dumping my bags at the hotel and walking across the road to soak up the adrenaline-fuelled atmosphere of the Expo on the afternoon before THE RACE. I had used the mobile to hook up with a couple of other bloggers who were at the Expo at the same time, Martin H a rugby player from near Manchester, who I had first met at the City of Manchester 10k last year, and who was a first-timer like me, and his Mum Mother H who was an old hand at this and there to do it for the fifth or sixth time. Eventually I tore myself away, and whereas earlier in the week the staff had been guarding the *goodie bags* at the exit with their very lives, they were now desperate to offload the rest to anyone and everyone who would take them away for them.

Back at the hotel, the company I had booked the package with were holding a get-together for their customers, and passed on a few great tips from their years of experience to make the day go smoother for us all. I headed up to my room and carefully laid everything out ready for the race, just as I had in Newcastle. The list was identical in every way, except for two key extras. The first was the new laces for my running shoes. About a week or two before the race, everyone who runs the London Marathon gets sent a lot of information about the day to help their planning. Included with this pack is a set of RED shoelaces, provided by the charity HEART UK, exclusively for London Marathon runners, and I had now installed these ready for the race. If you ever see a runner out on the roads who has red laces in their running shoes, take it as a sign that they have run the London Marathon, and they are wearing them with pride. The second addition to the list was a handful of Gels – small energy gel packs with rip-off seals to use as boosters during the run. The simple fact, as I know I have mentioned before, is that running a marathon will use up, according to the size and shape of the runner, anything up to, or even over, 4000 calories. The human body cannot physically store that much energy, so you have to adopt whatever strategies you can to make sure you don't *hit the wall*, where you reach that point where the body has simply run out of glycogen stores and however much you want to run, there is simply no fuel left in the tank to make the muscles move according to the brain's instructions. My strategy, along with many of the other runners, was to take an energy gel every few miles along the run. I would carry the first few in my belt pouch, and replenish them from my girls who would be waiting at The Prostate Cancer Charity Cheering Stations at around mile 14, and around mile 20. (This didn't mean they would have to run those 6 miles faster than me. While I was running the 6 miles on the big loop around Docklands and back, they would just have to cross the *neck* of the loop.) Once this was all set out ready, I wandered down to the restaurant to get my fill of one of the special pasta dishes they had laid on for the many runners staying there.

Just as I was finishing up, and wondering how on earth I was now going to fill the nervous few hours before I could at least start trying to go to sleep, I got a text from another blogger Angie K, asking me what I was doing. She was down in London for the run, and had her husband and two daughters, who were about the same age as my younger ones, with her. They were in the West End, and she quickly persuaded me to jump onto the DLR and meet them in Covent Garden, where we met at an occasional haunt of mine when I was in town called The Crusted Pipe, a pleasant wine bar downstairs in the old market. Neither of us was certain that going out in the West End of London drinking red wine was anywhere in the text books about preparing for your marathon run, but it certainly took our minds off the next morning, and her family did their best to keep changing the subject to more mundane matters (without much success!). Before it got too late I finally made my excuses and went in search of my bed.

Sunday 13th April 2008 dawned stunningly bright and still, if a little chilly, with a crystal clear blue sky. The weather could not have been more perfect for long distance running at that point, and it seemed the gods of running were on our side for once. The previous year had been the hottest race ever, and the water stations had run out leaving desperate runners begging water from concerned spectators down at the back of the race. This year was obviously going to be fine and clear, and the temperature would definitely not climb too high. A quiet and pensive atmosphere among runners in the dining room was offset by the *dawn chorus* of their kids anticipating an exciting day of spectating. Once kitted out, and with everything else stuffed into my baggage lorry duffle bag, I wandered down with ages to spare before the coach would leave. The hotel was alongside an old wharf off the River Thames, so I wandered along by the water, watching vapour trails criss-cross the perfect clear sky. Suddenly my mobile phone started buzzing, and the first of many text messages wishing me good fortune arrived with a shiver and a shake of the phone.

Just as I was herded onto the next coach, ready to be transported to my doom, I received another text. This one was from a lady blogger in Cheshire who went by the name of Kitten, and with whom I had been exchanging comments on the blogs almost since my very first blog post when she was a new blogger too. I had eventually met her and her family at that great bloggers meet The City of Manchester 10k the previous year, and since then she had displayed an amazing talent for sending me texts at just the right moment before my races, and her timing that morning was impeccable just as I was climbing onto the coach. The emotions of the impending challenge were at that point hitting the heights, so I sent her back what was to turn into an absolute classic text message once she immediately copied it onto a post on Realbuzz for all to see! The text I sent back simply read,

"OOOOOHHHHH SSSSSHHHHHIIIIITTTTT!!!!!"

This succinctly summed up the moment for me. I was later told that it had sent her into a fit of hysterical laughter from which she took some time to recover.

In no time we were deposited at Blackheath, and I commenced the long walk to find my start area. The FLM utilises different start areas for the Elite athletes, the Ballot runners and the Charity Bond Place runners to avoid too much congestion near the start. They all run the exact same distance but the routes don't finally merge until about three miles into the race. I headed for the charity area which was my designated start, and very soon came upon a large gathering of bloggers from Realbuzz for a pre-arranged meet next to the Lucozade Tent in the holding area. A few chats later, and having checked that Angie K had survived the previous night intact, I deposited my bag on the designated lorry, and we were told over the PA system to enter our pens, where adrenaline overload seemed to be the order of the day. According to my predicted time I was in the last but one pen, but unlike many runners I really don't mind where I start, it's the taking part that counts. Before we had any more time to think about it, we heard the klaxon go, and the race begins. We stand around a bit more, waiting for our pen to be released, and then begin the long, slow walk towards the gates of the park a few hundred yards ahead, through them and round to the left and another couple of hundred yards to the start line. As we shuffle along, a TV cameraman on a cherry picker high above the gates starts waving madly at the crowd of us below as he prepares to go live, so we all wave and scream back at him for the folks back home on their sofas. The thought flashes through my head that this is *where I always used to be... Oh My God – how life has changed*. It had taken 3½ years to make this utterly incredible journey from sofa to start line, from a 28 stone hulk to a 13 stone marathon runner. What odds would I have got for that bet, I wondered?

We shuffle through the gates, and the road became wider so we can finally start to jog towards the archway across that start line. Now we can hear the *whine* of the red computer sensor mat across the road, and we all push the buttons on our watches as we cross the line.

"I AM RUNNING THE LONDON MARATHON."

The first 9 or 10 miles I'm cruising along in a fair crowd, comfortable, trying not to overdo it, keep to my pace plan, keep hydrated, take a gel every 5 miles, applaud, like all the other runners, the bands are playing for us and there are disco parties outside every pub even at this time in the morning. The crowds are simply amazing, wall to wall people along both sides of the road. As we get to the merger point with the other runners from the Ballot start, both sides are good naturedly booing each other, and as it's a large road junction surrounded by shops and pubs there are huge crowds watching at this point.

There are portaloos placed along the course every few miles, but being gentlemen, of course, we leave these to the ladies and make the best we can of handy plantations when the need becomes overwhelming. There can surely be nothing more disheartening than standing in a queue for a portaloo with the time ticking away, but this can often be the inevitable side effect of keeping well hydrated.

Still cruising, about mile 10, maybe near enough two hours in or something near, when the beautiful crystal clear blue sky suddenly turns dark, menacing and then black. This does not look particularly good, but now that I am well warmed up and jogging along it is getting just a tiny bit on the warmish side so the runners friend – a little light drizzle, would not be entirely unwelcome. Unfortunately it isn't a little light drizzle, but a very substantial downpour of freezing sleet, accompanied by the ambient temperature falling through the floor like a lead balloon. This is disastrous for warmed up muscles, and before long we are all suffering as this arctic monsoon takes at least 15 minutes to pass, leaving the runners at that point knocked completely out of their stride and freezing in soaking wet sleet covered kit. I had been very comfortable in just my single thin running vest up to that point, but the next few miles were a struggle to get back up to running temperature, and get the muscles loose again.

Pottering along about the 12 mile mark, remembering to whip the camera out and get shots on the run of all the interesting things that caught my eye, and especially trying to get shots of the mile markers and the clocks on each one as a record of my run, I suddenly recognise Jamaica Road and realise we are about to turn onto Tower Bridge. This will be a *spectator hotspot* and is also one of the special *photo points*, so I unashamedly position myself on the road with as few runners around me as possible, and prepare to look my best running over the most famous in the bridge in the world. It's always looked so flat from a car or taxi, but there's quite an incline up to that bridge when you are trying to run and look good for the cameras at the same time. The crowds here are just awesome, as is the noise they make as they look out for your name on your running vest and scream personalised encouragements at every runner. As we come off the bridge, we have to turn right and head towards Docklands, even though we know that if we turned left here we would only be 2 or 3 miles from the finish line. As we head the other way, the faster runners are streaming past on the other carriage-way heading to the finish line, and must be at least 10 miles ahead of us travelling approximately twice as fast as we are, and they're not the *really* fast people who have probably already finished. Just down the road we pass the 20k sign, closely followed by the 13 mile marker, and then the HALF WAY sign. As some around me groan, I just decide it's all downhill from here (metaphorically) and look forward to spotting The Prostate Cancer Charity's cheering point ahead. One of the big sportswear manufacturers had kindly donated a huge number of T-shirts to them in their pale blue colour, with Prostate Cancer Charity Supporter printed on them, and they had supplied them to all the supporters of their runners. The idea was that they would all gather at the same point and cheer anyone in a Prostate Cancer running vest to give them a huge boost. All the charities did this sort of thing, and some of them even got sufficiently organised to make their points based at pubs. I very nearly ran right past them in the end, as they were in a fairly narrow part of the course there, but the girls saw me coming and were screaming at me enough to grab my attention. I took a brief stop, grabbed another drink from them, and a few more gels; reassured them that I was perfectly fine and enjoying it and hit the road again.

By now the effects of that ghastly sleet shower had finally disappeared, I was warmed through, well fuelled, jogging along nicely, and starting to feel extremely confident. I even began to watch out for the consternation on spectators' faces as they tried to scream out my name and realised they had no idea how to say TISM – the name I now always had on my running vests. I suppose it was a bit naughty, but I generally have it on my vests as ID to other bloggers running in the same races. As we came through amongst the towers of Canary Wharf the sky began to darken again, and the temperature commenced dropping like a stone again. Before long, as we wound our way back through the community streets of East London, the heavens opened and this time dumped a large mass of freezing sleet and snow on all the slower runners still in this area. At this point it slowly dawned on me that I could no longer feel my fingers, on either hand and that even though I was still jogging along, I was actually violently shivering at the same time. My worst fear at that point was that I could no longer hold a drink bottle from the water stations or a pouch from the Lucozade energy drink stations, and I couldn't get the gels out of my gel belt. It was going to get serious if I couldn't keep myself topped up, even though we were only maybe 8 miles from the finish. It would probably have been alright from this angle, but the psychology was the important thing at that point of the race.

The fabulous St John's Ambulance Service First Aid stations came to our rescue at just the right moment. Realising that the likelihood of cases of collapse from hypothermia was very high, they started unwrapping and handing out the featherweight foil emergency blankets to every runner, and telling us to wrap them round us as we ran to try to increase our core body temperature. I grabbed one and did as bidden, even wrapping my hands tightly into the corners as I ran with my arms crossed across my chest buried in silver foil. I reckon I ran for about 3 miles wrapped up like this, and could probably lay claim to running in fancy dress as a turkey ready for the Xmas day oven! Things started to get just a little hazy round about this point, and although I can recall a few key moments, I can't be sure how I was in between, or whether the memories are even in the right order!

I remember that when I started thinking that I would probably be all right without the blanket now, I noticed that all along the roadside, used blankets had been discarded by stuffing them between the railings, creating a weird silver foil barrier all along the side of the road. It was obvious that everyone had started to have the same thoughts at that point, and it occurred to me that while I was running in a blanket I wouldn't get any photos as my number was covered up, and no one was calling my name out as my name was covered too. At that point my blanket joined the foil wall, and I only regretted it for a short while as my body readjusted to the cold again.

At one point the route ran around a large roundabout, underneath a wide railway viaduct, which meant we were underneath it for a couple of minutes at least. Right in the middle of the roundabout itself was a group of extraordinary drummers, beating seven bells out of a set of enormous Chinese-style drums and the sound reverberated underneath the viaduct in an unbelievably physical barrage of sound. Those guys must have been beating those drums for hours, and I hope they understand the wonderful way that the sound picked up the runners, hurled us around that roundabout and spat us out with a gut-wrenching adrenaline boost which made everyone pick up the pace for at least a mile.

Somewhere around 19 miles I was verbally grabbed by the girls again, and picked up the last of my requirements to get me to the finish. I nearly missed them as they were positioned just past a bend near a pub, I think. They had been getting a bit anxious as I was now just a little behind schedule, but I was in no mood for hanging around for a chat and getting colder stood still, so I grabbed my bits and took off again, leaving them to find their own way back to the finish.

Then there was the extraordinary *orange tunnel* incident. At various points along the course, Lucozade energy drink stations were set up, where volunteers handed out small plastic pouches of orange-flavoured Lucozade Sport drink. The idea was to squeeze the drink through the spout, which helped prevent choking on it as you ran, and when you had had enough, you just threw the remains to the side of the road for the cleaners to collect later. Very few people actually squeeze the last drops out of these packs, and if any get trodden on by following runners they tend to ooze out their remains on to the road, and turn it just a little bit sticky. Under normal conditions this doesn't have much effect, but you sometimes notice one or two slightly sticky footsteps for a few hundred yards after an energy station. In their infinite wisdom, the organisers had positioned the last energy station immediately before the long underpass tunnel which eventually turns up onto the Embankment for the run down to the Houses of Parliament.

The stretch from the Tower of London to the Embankment was really bursting with spectators still making a huge amount of noise, even though this was now about 3 hours after the front runners had passed by. So by now we had covered probably about 24 miles already, had been enjoying a long stretch of raucous support, got a last pouch of energy drink, and then ran straight into the tunnel, which was lit solely by the strange orange streetlights in the roof. Added to this effect were the tens of thousands of discarded energy packs thrown to the side of the road by the 25,000 or more runners who had preceded us, all oozing their remaining contents slowly across the road. And YES – the packs were all bright orange, the contents were orange and by now the road was virtually orange. No spectators were allowed in the tunnel, so it had suddenly gone deathly quiet apart from the laboured gasps of the runners all around me and the sound of all the feet sticking to the road at every step. It was a totally surreal moment indeed, and an amazingly clear memory of it for all that.

Then we were running up the short rise out of the tunnel onto the Embankment itself beside the River Thames, and I could see Big Ben straight ahead through the trees. From that point to the finish the energy of the extraordinary crowds simply carried me home. As I approached the turn into Parliament Square someone let out an ear piercing shriek of "TISM" and I recognised another fellow blogger Supercaz, who had come along to support all the bloggers running, and had stood there for hours watching out just to give each of us that extra boost for the last mile. Running across Parliament Square with only about a mile to go my spirits were really lifted even more by the biggest crowd of the day, making the biggest racket of the day. I was all smiles now, grinning like the proverbial Cheshire Cat, as nothing would stop me now. I spotted one of the official photographers ahead of me, sitting on the ground in front of a bollard in the middle of the road, so I ran straight towards him with the smile on full wattage, in the absolute certainty that this was going to make a fabulous picture (it now hangs framed on my lounge wall, and is all the more stunning because that genius photographer had put himself there for the simple reason that he could frame his subjects as they ran towards him with Big Ben on their left shoulder – it is the ultimate photo of running London).

Now it was Birdcage Walk, 800 to go, 600 to go, 400 to go and coming round past Chelsea Barracks in front of Buckingham Palace the 26 mile marker with a huge banner draped across the front of the footbridge above our heads *385 Yards to go*. Onto The Mall and now I could see the finish line and I was still concentrating enough to REMEMBER TO SMILE FOR THE CAMERAS! Arms aloft and cross the line – officially 5 hours, 46 minutes, 05 seconds after I had crossed the Start Line.

STOP! This can actually prove to be quite difficult after that distance. I was directed to a little ramp, where some wonderful volunteers were sitting low down to remove our timing chips; then the medal placed round your neck; on to pose in front of one of the special backdrops for the photographers to get the *I've finished and here's my medal shot*; across the road to pick up a goodie bag which had a bottle of water, a bottle of energy drink, an apple, a bag of Mars Planets and all sorts of bits and pieces making a basic survival kit; keep moving towards the baggage lorries to get kit back; get bag, step away from lorry towards side of road, lean against a convenient tree; realise that you are about to pass out and stuff yourself with the chocolates, the energy drink, anything for the fastest possible energy hit (that's why they are in the goodie bag). Stabilise without falling over – but only just.

Then realise that walking straight towards you, with her kitbag and goodie bag, is Katie H, another blogger with whom I had been part of a double act of mutual support all spring, and we just stopped and hugged each other without saying a word. What an amazing coincidence, because in the chaos and crowds we could have taken ages if we had been deliberately trying to meet up. Then it was the long trek together down the rest of the Mall to the family reunion area on Horse Guards Parade, where my crew were waiting impatiently under the letter H. After a quick diversion to get a few photos with Katie's Crew, we set off in the cold and damp to the hotel near Victoria Station where The Prostate Cancer Charity had a large function room set up with hot drinks, snacks and that most wonderful combination of sheer luxury at that moment – massage tables and sports massage therapists. Two steaming mugs of coffee and a gorgeous leg massage later, I effected a quick change into some street clothes and we were off to Kings Cross for the train home, accompanied by medal spotting, and that silent exchange of smiles of respect and acknowledgement between the wearers.

I was now officially, and forever, a marathon runner. And I had another of these to do in six weeks! At least I now knew exactly what I was letting myself in for, but more fundamentally, I also knew that I could do it. The first half of my *Spring Double* was done, now onwards to the other half.

First thing to do on the Monday was to get photos to the local paper of their round-up of local runners who had done the run. By now the word was out that I was The Ambassador for The Great Eastern Run, so I updated the website with that piece of news, and added my race report to the ever growing collection on there. I had written a post on my blog about this appointment, and as a result a number of bloggers had entered the race already, and a couple of them had even decided that although they were not ready to attempt a half marathon, they would come along anyway and registered as volunteers to help marshal the race. This was just typical of the quite phenomenal community spirit that had grown up amongst the Realbuzz bloggers over the last year or so.

To be perfectly honest I did very little training for the next week or so, but managed to get in some very good quality steam room and Jacuzzi sessions. Over the past few months I had evolved a theme on my blog characterising my running as a basic long term battle between ME (my brain and personality) and THE ORGANISM (my body, which constantly tried to get out of doing too much). If I got in a really good long training run I would often take a rest day the next day as per all the good training plans, and I now referred to these as Organism Pamper Days (OPDs for short) when a rest day was enhanced by a session in the steam room or Jacuzzi at the gym. I had noticed that the term had now been adopted by many folk on the blogs as different runners referred to taking OPDs when they made entries on their blogs. Well I can only describe the week after the Flora London Marathon as a full scale Organism Pamper WEEK, where I relaxed all the rules, allowed myself some *treats* on the dietary front, and generally indulged The Organism in any way it wanted. Running a marathon takes a lot out of a body, quite literally, and it does no harm whatsoever to allow it some serious healing time.

However, all good things must come to an end, and Edinburgh was getting closer and closer and nothing was going to stop that process. I started to get some short runs in and check that everything was still in full working order with no obvious after effects lingering in the shadows waiting to pounce. By the end of April I was back on schedule, or at least back running as smoothly (if you could ever call my running *smooth*) as ever. I actually had no idea what training to do to cover a six week gap between marathons, as it turned out to be something that very few people attempted. In the end I decided to just keep my fitness levels up, put in one good long run every Sunday and a couple of shorter ones during the week. Nothing I could do in that short period of time would have any fundamental effect on my core fitness or running speed, so there was no point in pushing boundaries.

May was going to be a busy month whichever way I looked at it. The only free weekend I had was the first weekend of the month, so I made sure I got a good run, and then generally took it easy. The second weekend I drove across to Southport on the North-West coast just north of Liverpool for my nephew's wedding. The ceremony was in Kirby, but the do was at a hotel in Southport and all the families from across the country were staying at the hotel to keep life simple (and avoid driving *under the influence*). I was to be there from the Friday afternoon till the Sunday, with a very long drive indeed there and back.

We had a great weekend, and the weather was extremely kind to everyone. I had taken my running kit with me, as it had seemed like a great chance to get a run along the famous promenade there next to the sea, but the weekend had been meticulously planned and I rapidly realised that no allowance had been made for any *free time*. The word had been put out about my weight loss and running, and it seemed that everyone there wanted to have a chat about it. I had actually packed my

London Marathon medal to show my Mum, but it proved a tricky job to keep an eye on it as it got handed round at every opportunity. To be honest, during the Saturday evening dance, when the numbers had swelled considerably with everyone who couldn't fit into the church, I actually retrieved it and went and hid it in my room for fear of losing it completely. It was a great weekend, but I was relieved to complete the long drive home and settle back into a routine in the run up to the next marathon.

By now the entries to this year's Great North Run had been sorted out, with Number Four getting very lucky with a place through the *Daily Telegraph special first 2000 for readers ballot*, Number Three and Number Four's boyfriend getting main ballot places, and Number Three's boyfriend having to resort to my arranging for him to get one of The Prostate Cancer Charity's Bond places. He was always going to run for them even if he got a ballot place, not out of some misguided loyalty to me, but because his Grandfather had been a victim of it. Once we got them into some serious training runs, it was quickly confirmed that Number Three and Number Four's boyfriend would not be able to manage the training with their respective ankle and knee conditions, but the other two were coming along fine.

So on the 18th May, just a week before the Edinburgh Marathon, Number Three's boyfriend and I headed out to run The Deepings 10k, which for me was the anniversary of my very first race. The excuse I shall give for the completely devastating distance by which he beat me is simply that he is a fit young man in his early twenties, and there would have been something severely wrong if he hadn't soundly beaten me. At least I managed to beat my own time from the previous year by a minute and a half, so left with some dignity still intact. I know it wasn't perfect training by any manner of means, but I have a great affection for that race, and the fun I had there the first time round, and it is good to support local small races which are, really, the lifeblood of the sport throughout the country.

On the Wednesday I had to go in to see the surgical team for my pre-operation checks, and was relieved to find that they were perfectly satisfied with all the tests and declared me a *suitable case for treatment*. I think they were referring to the operation there, and not making some oblique reference to the two marathons. Thursday was spent checking that I had everything I would need for three nights in Edinburgh, plus all my race kit. This again was an Expo race, so I didn't have my bib number and chip yet, but was intending to collect it when I got to the Expo on Saturday morning.

I travelled up on the train on the Friday afternoon, and checked in to the hotel where I would be staying. It was in The Grassmarket, right opposite The Mussel and Steak House where we had enjoyed our annual Xmas lunch, and where we had coincidentally booked for dinner that night. Some of the boys would be working on race day, and one was away somewhere, so we had opted for an *informal* gathering on the Friday, mainly because I didn't trust myself in their hands the night before a marathon. One of the main topics on the agenda that night was planning the October trip to Spain as we would all be together with diaries ready. To start the process, they now knew to check with me whether I was racing, so I told them that I would be doing the Great North Run on the 5th October, and the Great Eastern Run on the 12th October. Jokingly they asked if I had any others planned, and I casually mentioned that although I didn't yet have an official entry bought and paid for until after that weekend's run, I was thinking about possibly doing The Athens Classic Marathon on 11th November. I had to explain what the race was all about, and they immediately understood why I was interested in doing it. At that point, the Auld Git threw into the conversation that he had never actually been to Athens before, and soon it was established that none of us had been there before. We'd all been to one or other of the islands, but never to Athens itself. The decision then followed fairly quickly that the Spanish trip would be abandoned this year, as the boys had decided to come to Athens instead. By now I was bowing to the inevitable, and knew that I was definitely going to be having a go at it this year, rather than in later years. All I had to do was survive another round of surgery, get healed up and back into training as soon as possible after the operation, and then get fit enough for another marathon within about 4½ months of the operation - which this time would have been carving up my LEGS! No problem then.

The Expo on the Saturday morning meant a long haul down to Leith, where it was being held in an indoor sports centre. It was probably the saddest, sorriest excuse for an Expo you would ever come across, and once I had collected my race pack it took all of five minutes to see everything. The only giveaways were in the goodie bag handed out at the exit, and whilst I am certain that the pack of the sponsors very own baking potatoes was of the topmost quality, I quickly decided that I was not prepared to lug them round for the rest of the day and so declined the kind offer. Just as I was about to join the mass rapid exit I spotted one of my very special blogger friends, Russell Nimbus from Liverpool, with his wife, about to pick up his race pack. I had been quite involved in his decision to run this race as his first marathon, and we had plans to meet for dinner the following night after the race. We got the obligatory photos done, and I left them to *enjoy* the rest of the Expo and went to find a ride back into the city. This proved damn nearly impossible as there were massive queues at the bus stops and quite clearly no additional services laid on to cope, which should have been a no-brainer with 11,000 runners and their supporters all having to arrive and depart from that bus stop in 2 days. I am now given to understand that they have abandoned the idea of an Expo in future and will be mailing out the race packs.

After a quiet night I was up with the lark (which was singing with a definite Lothian brogue on that fine morning), had a light breakfast, and then headed off to the start area in full running kit. It was wonderful to be able to get ready in the room and then just stroll across town towards the start at a respectable time, and the crowds grew as I neared the launch pad. The whole start area was cramped and thoroughly disorganised, but I eventually bored my way through the glutinous mass of bodies to the relative quiet of the last pen. As the pens and road here were very narrow, we were stretched a very long way back from the start, and it took a few minutes of jogging once we were released to even get a sight of the start line and hear the familiar whine of the sensor mat. I knew that there would be TV and newspaper cameras in abundance at this point, so decided to run alongside a very large rhinoceros running for the WWF as it would be a camera magnet at this point. The crowds were immense here, and making a really good racket as we took off down a long slow decline away from the city centre, and I remember thinking that with all the wonderful sights and architecture in Edinburgh we seemed to be pursuing a route which would carefully avoid all of them, which was such a shame. Almost as soon as we were out of sight of the start line the crowds quickly dwindled to virtually nothing, and the route wound through some *edge of city light industry* areas as the runners became strung out into a thin ribbon.

We passed the new parliament building, almost without realising it, then headed off down to Portobello Promenade straight into the teeth of a half gale whipping up the Firth of Forth and creating a nice sand-blasting effect as it crossed the beach. What followed was 14 miles along the coast road, straight into the teeth of that wind, with the added benefit of really strong sunshine as the day progressed. The horizon for much of that stretch was *artistically* dominated by the massive twin chimneys of Cockenzie Power Station, whose motivational properties still continue to elude the most diligent of seekers after truth. They had conspired to include a ghastly mile or two on farm tracks with lurking ankle breaking stones strewn about to make life interesting, which took us through the Gosford Park Estate, and then it was across the front lawn of the big house, through a wood and back on the coast road to run all the way back to Musselburgh Racecourse for the finish. Of course, having made the turn at about 18–19 miles, the wind immediately dropped for us slower runners so we didn't have it on our backs for the last 7 miles after all, just the ever strengthening sun.

There was a stretch here of a mile or two where the out and back routes shared the same road, and as I was heading back through Longniddry Bents I spotted the unmistakeable blogger Kizzi 10000 still coming along in the other direction. We had been chatting on the site for ages, as she was another weight loss wonder woman, but had never actually met before despite our best efforts, and she spotted me about the same time. Race etiquette about crossing over the centre line went straight out the window as we both veered straight towards each other and indulged ourselves with a huge hug, before plodding on.

Shortly after this my shins began to ache quite seriously, which dictated a slow final section with a few walk breaks, and by now there weren't even noisy gatherings of supporters outside the pubs we passed, just the odd policeman, first aider or marshal to give us a little bit of support. Of course those architectural masterpieces atop the power station added their own special flavour to the majority of that return leg, but once I passed them again I knew the finish was not too far.

Eventually I painfully passed one last pub, rounded a corner and the racecourse appeared and lifted my spirits. No countdown markers here, but the route turned in through the fence and then we were on a temporary surface over the grass of the home straight in front of the now sparsely populated stands, and with a clear road ahead I made one last sprint for the finish with my arms raised. Regrettably, 10 yards further on there was a sharp right turn guarded jealously by some iron barriers, but this supertanker by now had a much wider turning circle and longer stopping distance, so I just ran right into the barriers as the most effective solution to stopping. 5 hours 54 minutes and 57 seconds after crossing the start I finally brought the race to an end.

Then it was chip removal, medal, water and a banana. The highly professional photography team the organisers had contracted had gone for a cuppa, so there was no chance of a *medal at the finish* photo in front of the very nice backdrops set up there. So I wandered through to the baggage lorries, picked up my kit, and then hooked up with a local blogger Lynda L who had been on finish line volunteer duty for most of the day. She kept her promise and plied me with some wonderful jelly babies as we sat in the sun and chatted for a while. Now Musselburgh Racecourse is a good few miles out of Edinburgh, so the final delight was the massive queue for the shuttle bus service back to the start, where standing on the side of a road in a slowly shuffling mass of knackered runners and by now bored supporters was just what the doctor would have ordered for my shattered legs.

After the stiff-legged shuffle back across the Royal Mile to the hotel, and the miracle cure of a long hot shower, I was raring to go again and grabbed a taxi for the hop to the Omar Khayyam at Haymarket. Way back in the distant past, before I started on the weight loss project, I adored Indian food (or at least the variety served in the UK). Although I could never understand the attraction of the nuclear fusion in your mouth variety, the more elegant flavours of the subtle end of the menu were where I found pleasure. Such delights had been one of the first casualties of the healthy eating regime, but remained firmly fixed at the head of the *soul food* list, and it had now become my *celebration meal of choice* for after big races. When you've just run a marathon, burnt off over 4,000 calories, and are in dire need of a well deserved treat, then the answer is an Indian meal. Russell and Marie didn't stand a chance on this, so we had booked this restaurant, weeks before, as I had eaten there on numerous occasions in the past. It was the perfect way to recover from a difficult day, and Russell was justifiably on a real high after completing his very first marathon.

An exceptionally good nights sleep, and a relaxed train ride home on the Bank Holiday the next day, and the Spring Double was in the bag. Once I'd got the washing machine buzzing away, I popped to the club for what was almost becoming a ritual session in the steam room and Jacuzzi, and wondered about the next operation in a fortnight. I was beginning to look forward to getting this thing over and done with once and for all. For the last 3½ years life had been completely dominated by weight targets, the running bet with Dr Ken, then the upcoming reconstructive surgeries. Right now I was just a fortnight away from the LAST operation, I was at my desired weight and I was fitter than I had ever been.

Back home, I went straight on to the internet and booked a place in The Athens Classic Marathon. Then I emailed the boys to tell them I have an entry and am definitely doing it! After all, what's life without an exciting target or two?! The Spring Double had been done, now it was a case of:

"Bring on the Autumn Treble. Great North Run 5th October, Great Eastern Run 12th October, and Athens Classic Marathon 11th November! WOW!"

CHAPTER NINETEEN

THE FINAL CUTS

THERE WAS SIMPLY NO REAL POINT IN DOING ANY SERIOUS TRAINING FOR the next couple of weeks, bearing in mind that I was about to have my legs carved up and would be out of action for an indeterminate period. So I took it fairly easy and just got on with the daily grind. A couple of days before I was due to go into Addenbrookes Hospital again for the Reconstructive Surgery unit to do their thing, I was wondering how long I could expect to be in this time, and in the end I just called them to find out. Mr Gillespie, my new consultant surgeon, wasn't available, but another of the team was happy to have a chat. He told me that I should reckon on probably three days after the operation, and then added:

"But as this particular operation is highly susceptible to many complications, you should be prepared for potentially a longer stay."

This probably well meaning remark left me absurdly worried. If this operation was more prone to problems than the last one, and last time I ended up still in hospital three weeks after the operation, was this going to be worth the risk? The stomach skin had been a huge problem, and the removal had without doubt fundamentally made my life easier, but this time it was nowhere near as crucial for me. I started to question the whole rationale for having this surgery, and debated with myself whether to just cancel it and forget about it. I got out my file of the hospital letters, and was checking through the details when I came across the letter from the Board of the Primary Care Trust which said:

"This procedure is included within the Low Priority Procedures list. As such we do not normally fund this procedure, but will do so if there are exceptional individual circumstances.

Having carefully considered the clinical information regarding the above named patient, and in view of his substantial weight loss, I can confirm that we will fund this patient to have an open T scar thigh lift."

This got me thinking that I was a very lucky man to have my local PCT be prepared to spend an awful lot of money getting one of their top surgeons to perform this operation on me. This was obviously a once in a lifetime opportunity to finish the job properly, and the sensible thing was to bite the bullet and get it over and done with once and for all. With that in mind, on the 10th June I presented myself to Ward L5 in the Addenbrookes Treatment Centre and was immediately greeted with a cheery:

"Hello again, Mike, we've been expecting you. A Bay, bed 4 – you know the drill and how to find it. Make yourself at home and someone will be along with a coffee in a few minutes."

Talk about being put at ease! The staff were pretty much, the same crew as last autumn and for some reason mostly remembered me well. I introduced myself to my fellow inmates in the bay, unpacked my bits and pieces and popped to the machine at the end of the ward to pay the extortionate fees for a five day card which would turn on the TV and phone over the bed. I never actually used their phone on any stay, as contrary to my expectation it was perfectly fine to use mobile phones anywhere on the ward.

Mr Gillespie came round for a final pre-operation chat when he had finished his list for the day, and if I hadn't known better I would have fallen into the trap of thinking he was having one last go at putting me off completely. While he was making sure I was in sufficiently good working order to withstand the rigours of his handiwork the next morning, he dropped a classic comment into the conversation:

"Of course the area where we will be operating is the most difficult area to get to heal properly anywhere on the body, so you'll have to be very careful and not move much for a while."

I was about to rise to his bait when I thought better of it. It was way too late to be backing out now, so I resigned myself to my fate and tried extremely hard to forget about it. I got myself a sandwich, and settled down for the night. In the morning of course it was back on the *nil by mouth* routine and strict instructions not to go anywhere as they could come for me at any time.

Finally the theatre porter arrived, unplugged my bed, (they were all *magic* electric beds, with a remote control thing which could send it into all manner of contortions), and we were off on the familiar route to the Carvery. The chatty sleep therapist had me under in a flash...

Recovered some semblance of consciousness back at base again, and was immediately given some fairly strict instructions not to try to move about, to drink as much as possible, and "use the bottles". I promised to comply with lying still instantly, and for as long as they wanted, but pointed out politely that I would need them to go and get me a good strong coffee and a jug of iced water if I was to comply with the drinking instruction. They also kindly offered to order me dinner, which was possible at later hours for immediate post-op patients, but by now I knew that was not a sensible option if you wanted something edible. The alternative was a completely free choice from their entire stock of sandwiches, which meant cheese on white bread, but also meant speedy and filling, so it became the chosen solution. Drips on hooks, attached to needles in the back of my hand, with new bags regularly – each one accompanied by a variety of pills, and frequent vital signs checks just about sum up that night.

Woken very early, before everyone else, for more bags to empty through needles in the back of the hand, but at least I got a wake up hot drink. I was still not allowed to move, so it was all really boring for a while. Just before morning rounds one of the nurses came along and removed some of the dressings which were no longer as clean as they might have been, and I got to sneak a look at a corner of the handiwork. Much to my consternation, the top few inches of the cut on my right thigh didn't seem to have any stitches in, and was a very neat thin line indeed. My first thought (and it probably sums up the state of my brain at that time of the morning) was to wonder just how long I had been asleep, as it almost looked as though the wound was healed already. My query to the Eastern European agency night nurse was rebuffed with instructions to ask the doctors when they came on their morning rounds.

One of the distinct advantages of Bay A was that we were always first on those morning rounds, and as the catering girls usually made everyone wait for breakfast till they had been seen by the Medics, that put us at the head of the queue and more likely to get properly hot drinks and fresh toast. So it wasn't long till the white coats began to gather, and I could raise my query. The explanation was very straightforward.

"That part of this particular operation wound probably wouldn't be able to take stitches without problems, so we use superglue instead at that point."

I'd got quite used to getting stitched up by the team in there, but when they started to resort to superglue you had to wonder what things were coming to. But once I got to see the whole area of the wounds on both legs, I realised that they had glued about 5 inches at the top of each leg, and the rest was good old fashioned dissolving stitches. Just for the sake of clarity, I should point out that the operation had officially been a *bi-lateral thigh lift*, the purpose of which was to remove the redundant loose skin on the inner thighs. The wounds started at the very top of the front of my thighs, cut straight right round to the top of the inside edge of my thighs, and then down the inner thigh to not far short of my knees. Each leg had a scar about 14 inches long, which significantly enhanced my score in the *show your scars* stakes! Not, you understand, that these particular scars were suitable for too much display, bearing in mind their *sensitive* location.

While I was having the dressings cleaned up first thing, I had noticed something completely unexpected. Quite apart from all the dressings that I had obviously expected down the thighs, I also had some large dressings at the outer extremities of each hip, roughly around the ends of the old scars from the first bit of work. Now seemed to be an appropriate moment to wonder what on earth these were there for, as I couldn't see the slightest connection.

"Oh – while I had you on the table, and I was *on a roll* with everything going superbly, I thought I might as well have your *dog ears* off as well. It was a sort of tidy up, while the going was good."

"Err fine, thanks." was about the most erudite response I could muster at that point. This was utterly amazing, and I just didn't know what to say next. It was certainly something that I had never thought would ever be sorted out. Yes, I knew they were there, but, compared to what was there before, these were insignificant, and the thought of removing them had never once crossed my mind.

Dog ears is obviously a highly technical, medical term in the field of reconstructive surgery, so I'll try to explain. When they removed the loose skin from my stomach the previous year, they had more or less cut out a large *3 leaf clover* shape, and then just pulled the edges together and sewn them up. If you have ever tried to do this with paper, or some sort of material or cloth, you'll readily know that the point where you start to pull the edges together gets a little rucked up around the end of the cut, and there's nothing you can do about it. Well the same applies to skin; the result of the operation was a quite small but marked *wing* around the very ends of the scars on each of my hips (or *dog ears* in surgical parlance). Once they have settled down, as mine had, apparently you can then get rid of them by doing a mini repeat operation, just through the dog ear itself, which restores the area to smooth and flat. This was precisely what he had done, while I was there on the table, so I had small dressings on each hip covering about six inches of new stitches on each side. They should heal up very quickly, and I would probably not be able to notice any new scars in the end as he had carefully married them up to the old scars. Don't you just love a man who takes pride in his work?!

The rest of the day passed in mind-numbing boredom, interspersed with even more mind-numbing short busts of daytime TV. Every now and again I was ministered to from the drugs trolley, or the coffee trolley, usually just a minute or two after I had finally managed to doze off. All in all not what one would call a fun day, and eventually it passed, lights were out, and I tried to get some sleep.

Friday was an altogether different affair. Morning rounds brought up the big question,

"Why haven't you got up yet?"

"I was told not to move, to give the legs a chance to heal properly."

"That was yesterday. Today is *get up and get cracking* day."

He then checked the little drains sticking out of each leg just beyond the end of the main wounds and decided that they could come out later as well. That was something to really look forward to then. If last time was anything to go by that should be more painful than the operation, and heaven knows where these ones went inside. In fact the possibilities there didn't bear thinking about!

Remarkably, I managed to get mobile again without too much fuss and bother; the pain pills were obviously doing their job extremely well. I was frankly petrified about having the drains removed, after the intense pain with the last lot, but again these were not too bad. The main problem was the act of standing up or sitting down. Once vertical I was OK, even if I did need a *slow moving vehicle* sign on my back! I had also figured out from my working knowledge of the place that I would almost certainly be kicked out the next day, so I put Number Three on notice, and managed to waste the rest of the day failing as usual to complete the Daily Telegraph crossword (one day I will – if dreams do really come true!).

Saturday morning brought the inevitable order of the boot, even though there was one area on my right thigh which was still playing up a little. But I got a right talking-to from Mr Gillespie, who had come by especially to see me even though it was a Saturday.

"I know by now exactly what you are like! So let's have no misunderstandings here. You are absolutely not, under any circumstances, to come even close to doing anything that in any way might be construed as running until I personally give you permission. Is that understood? Have I made my instruction plain enough for you?"

I think I got the message, and it turned out during the conversation that he did really know what it is like. He and his wife had both got entries to the Flora London Marathon 2008, but had to defer when she became pregnant. They were now looking to run it in 2009. He had already run the Jungfrau Marathon, and was about to do so again later in the year, so this guy was a serious runner indeed.

So I was duly ejected with the usual mathematical conundrum of the pill collection, a bag of extremely long dressings, and some strange brown pads in foil packets to put over the bit that was still leaking. I also had instructions to attend the dressing clinic at the Edith Cavell Hospital in Peterborough the following week. I persuaded Number Four to do some shopping, and then settled down for a quiet evening, and what turned out to be a comfortable night. I was religiously taking the antibiotics like clockwork, but as the painkillers were optional I opted not to take them. I did have a couple of paracetamol before turning in, but that was the last I took of any sort of pain relief. It was astounding how such a large operation, leaving me with a sum total of over 30 inches of stitches on my thighs and sides, could be done in such a way that, 72 hours later I was feeling fine and in very little pain at all.

I was still worried about possible infections, especially after having been dragged back into hospital for another 10 days last time. I kept a very close eye on the wounds, or at least as close as I could when I wasn't supposed to touch the dressings, and whilst the left leg seemed to be healing very quickly and more or less perfectly, the same could not be said for the right leg. I had to constantly change one particular area of the wound, just beyond where the stitches took over from the glue. I was also developing a swelling about the size of an egg a little further down the thigh, and a smaller one in a similar spot on the left leg. When I went in to the dressing clinic on the Friday they thought it wasn't too bad, but I had to go back again early the following week for another check. This time they were a little more concerned, and after a telephone call to the ward at Addenbrookes I was sent straight down there again for them to have a proper look. I absolutely refused to accept that the same thing was happening, and in defiant mood I went down with nothing to facilitate a stay. Perhaps a bit daft, under the circumstances, but I was determined not to give them the slightest excuse if they weren't totally convinced I should stay.

As luck would have it, they just poked around a bit, washed it, dressed it again, and sent me packing with a huge smile of relief. I suppose I should have been annoyed at being sent on an 80 mile round trip wild goose chase by train and taxi, but I was too happy at having escaped with my freedom to feel resentment. They were only trying to ensure my well being, after all.

To take my mind off all this, the 28th June was the first of the Expo things for the Great Eastern Run, which meant having a big display up in the centre of Queensgate, the big shopping centre in the middle of Peterborough. The idea was to encourage people to take part in either the main half marathon, or the 5k Fun Run, and at the same time try to recruit as many volunteers for the day as well. The stands were to be open from 10 till 4, and I had especially arranged for The Prostate Cancer Charity to have a free stand, so two of the community fund raising team were coming up for the day with all their display stuff. No one had given me the slightest idea of what was expected of me, except to be there, but someone had suggested I bring my medals, so I took along the Great North Run medal, the Flora London Marathon medal and the Edinburgh Marathon medal just in case.

When I finally pitched up a little late, excusing myself on the basis of the legs still being swathed in dressings, they were already set up and chatting to a few people, so I just wandered across and browsed through the literature they had prepared for the run. I hadn't seen any of it yet, and they had various leaflets about the details of the run, the fun run, volunteering, and the regular fortnightly training runs on Wednesday evenings starting from my gym, by coincidence. The gym people were there as well, with a stand offering free blood pressure and heart rate checks, and promoting the gym, obviously. As I was browsing, I realised that practically all the leaflets had either my photo and a paragraph or two about me, or a reference to me being the ambassador. I was quite surprised at how much they had involved me, but slightly miffed that no one had given me a chance to see what they were printing about me. I checked it through thoroughly and at least they hadn't printed anything wrong.

The team on the stand was made up of representatives of a couple of charities inviting people to run for their charity, some reps for some of the local running clubs which helped to organise the event and organised the training runs, and the sports development team from the city council whose *baby* this really was. Before I could work out what I was supposed to be doing, I found myself being drawn into various conversations and introduced with the leaflets which had my photos on. Apart from a short break for a sandwich and a drink for lunch, I was pretty much on my feet and chatting to people right through virtually to 4pm, and it was only when I finished that I realised it had probably been too much, really. But it had been a lot of fun, and if people were to be believed, and they weren't just humouring me, then my involvement was having the desired effect and people were actually signing up for the run with my story as their motivation. Whichever applied, I know it all made ME feel good that evening with my legs up and a glass of wine in my hand (purely for medicinal purposes, you understand – full of good anti-oxidants).

About this time I received an email out of the blue, (or out of cyberspace, anyway) from a public relations firm wanting to see if I would phone them about possibly doing some publicity stuff about my blog. I had no idea who they were, but as they mentioned the blog I thought I'd call and see what it was all about. It transpired that they were the agency for Realbuzz, the blogging site, and they wanted to do some bits and pieces to try to get more people onto the site and start blogging. They said that they had asked me because my blog was one of the most popular blogs on the whole site, and got one of the highest numbers of visitors, (plus it was a very interesting story). Not really knowing what to expect, but always having had tremendous support and motivation from all the users of the site, and never having had to pay anything to use the site, it seemed only fair to help out, so I agreed to go ahead. They prepared some notes to send out to people, and I checked them through, and then promptly more or less forgot about it.

Eventually I got to see the surgeon again exactly one month, to the day, after the operation. This time it was not one of the team, it was actually Mr Gillespie himself, and in between telling me about his preparations to run the Jungfrau Marathon in September, he prodded and poked around the undressed wounds. When he felt the swollen areas on each leg, he thought about them for a minute, then grabbed a needle and shoved it straight into the right leg, and then proceeded to use a plunger to draw out a lot of some clear liquid. As he did so, the swelling went right down, so he repeated the exercise on the left leg, with the same success.

"You are producing more lymph (*or something that sounded like that*) than you can currently get rid of naturally."

I was told he might have to do this again, or it might now be OK; there was no way of knowing for sure. The left leg in all other respects was fine now, well healed up and the bit that had been glued looked really neat and tidy to the point where I seriously wondered why they don't just glue everything if the scars look that good. No doubt they have their reasons, but I wasn't going to try to find them out now. The right leg was not doing so well, with one section of about an inch of the stitches having opening itself up, and this was going to require constant re-dressing to keep it clean and avoid the risk of infection. I decided that I just had to ask about getting back into training, even though with the leg not healing properly it was obviously still going to be some time. I really needed to know whether I could sensibly still target doing the runs lined up in October, especially the Great Eastern Run as I was now all over the literature, and they had put up that big section on the website too.

He told me that the legs were coming on really well (I would have hated to see what they would have been like if they were doing badly), and he thought that I should probably be able to start a bit of treadmill work *quite soon* and then build up at whatever speed I could manage from there, as long as it felt comfortable.

"But what do you mean by soon? Next week? Next month?"

"How would tomorrow suit?" was his astonishing response! I couldn't believe it, but he was perfectly serious, as long as I was careful and stopped at the slightest adverse reaction. The right leg was dressed once again, but the left leg was now OK on its own, and with that I was politely shown the door, with a request to drop in again in two weeks to see how things were doing.

It just goes to show what a remarkable thing the body truly is. On 11th June my thighs were carved open from hip almost to knee, the loose skin was cut out and the edges pulled together, stitched and glued up, and on 12th July there I was, back on the treadmill in the gym, doing 15 minutes at 5 mph for the first session, exactly as per the fine details of his instructions. I had to wear my short running tights, just to help hold it all together, and as I finished with a short cool down I noticed that they had ridden up a bit when running and a large slice of gauze and micropore was now uncovered, but nobody seemed to have noticed.

Best of all was the feeling that the surgery was now over and done with. The end was in sight.

CHAPTER TWENTY

A TALE OF TWO HALVES

WHEN I STEPPED ONTO THAT TREADMILL AGAIN, I CONFESS THAT I HAD NO idea how my legs were going to react. Not only was I worried about whether they would be OK after the operation in a general sense, but I was really concerned about whether they would be able to cope with the level of training that I was going to have to put in. At that point, I was just 12 weeks from the Great North Run, 13 weeks from the Great Eastern Run and 17 weeks from The Athens Classic Marathon, and my ability to get to their start lines was dependent upon my still having retained a good level of core fitness since having a break after Edinburgh. I knew I would have lost a lot, you can't go that long with no exercise at all without losing a lot of fitness, but as long as I hadn't got too much actual muscle wastage I could probably bring myself back up to scratch fairly quickly. Various studies have been done looking at how quickly you lose fitness when you reduce your training habits, but the results are a bit varied depending on whether you reduce frequency, duration or intensity. Not much has been done on what happens to your fitness when you grind it down to absolute zero in all directions, and have your legs carved up into the bargain, so this would have to be my own personal research project.

As luck would have it, and not a little obviously down to the incredible skills of Mr Gillespie, I was fine after that run, and quickly built up the distance each day. The strangest thing of all was that the more days I ran, the better the legs seemed to be healing up, and the small problem area finally closed itself up to the point where I could stop using dressings on it. Admittedly every now and again it would flare up again, and a new little hole would develop and leak all manner of obnoxious substances, so I always carried a small spare dressing or two, just in case.

The following week brought home to me with a bang what I had casually agreed to with the Realbuzz people. They had sent out their press release with my details, and all of a sudden the phone hardly stopped ringing. The first thing that was needed was a photoshoot with one of the big news agencies which had picked up the story, but they were absolutely gutted that I didn't have any of my original clothes from when I was at my biggest, as they do love their pictures of *thin guy in huge old trousers and shirt*. I explained that I had never actually expected to need them for anything like this, but they compromised by checking on what size I had been, and promptly going shopping for a pair of trousers and a shirt. Well, the media is all about creating images, isn't it! Before he left after an intense two hours of photography in a nearby park, I managed to achieve two results for myself. I got him to let me have some of the photos that the agency decided not to use, and I also got him to make a present of the trousers and shirt to me, as I now wished I had kept some once I had seen that size on me again.

As a result of all this activity there was a full page article in *The Daily Mirror*, another in *The Daily Telegraph* online, and on the Wednesday I had an ITV camera crew dragging me around for a shoot alongside the river. When they came back to the flat for some footage of a conversation in front of the computer with my blog on show, we coincided with Number Four coming in and she rapidly became the centre of attention and got herself on the TV too. Mind you, with her thespian talents she has always had a built-in light that turns on whenever a camera points in her direction, so I was beautifully upstaged but didn't care a bit. The profile film was broadcast on their local evening news programme and I was delighted with the piece they had created. Within a couple of days the Realbuzz PR people had taken the footage from the TV, added some titles back and front, a bit of music over their intro bits, and it was on Youtube, which was a first for me. A few radio interviews filled the gaps for a day or two, until it all started to die down again.

On the 27th July we had another Expo day for the Great Eastern Run, this time in Cathedral Square in the centre of Peterborough, and it was a scorching hot day. I spent the day again, with my medals round my neck, chatting to all and sundry and signing up runners for the race. Apparently their publicity about the Expo, as a place to get your race entry done with a small discount, had included a mention about meeting me. Although I had been chatting to people on the blog, and also through the message facility on my website, it was a whole new experience to meet real live people in the flesh who wanted to talk about it. When they asked me to be The Ambassador, it had seemed just like another piece of publicity someone wanted to use my story for, but this was actually starting to bring home to me with a sizeable clout that complete strangers were genuinely interested in what I had done, and wanted to do similar things, if on a smaller scale, as a direct result of my having done it. People were actually signing up for the half marathon or even just the 5k Fun Run, just because of me. This was getting very personal, and I wasn't sure how to react, but I knew it felt good.

Next day was another visit to Mr Gillespie, and another needle session in the swellings, which had returned but nowhere near as badly as before. He got less *stuff* out of them, and thought that they probably wouldn't need doing again. I also got the all-clear to start running outside again, when he realised how well it was going on the treadmill. As a runner himself, he was well aware of how ghastly running on a treadmill is compared to the real thing. We talked about this for a bit, and I explained to him that I only usually get on a treadmill for speed work sessions. These are a very useful part of any running training programme, where you alternate between sustained sprints, and slower recovery bits. Typically I would run at about 5 miles an hour to get warmed up, then do 2 minutes at 6 mph, 1 minute at 4mph, 2 minutes at 6.1, and increase the speed intervals by 0.1 mph each time up to around 7 mph, and then back down again. It was quite intense, and over time it had the effect of slightly increasing your normal running pace, and improving your endurance. The speed controls and clock on the treadmills in the gym made it possible to do these sessions very accurately, which was virtually impossible outside where you had to rely much more on guess work. They were also a lot less boring than just plodding away in the heat of the gym going nowhere not very fast.

August was a fairly quiet time, going for my training runs in later in the day when it was cooler, and generally making good progress towards the big Autumn Triple. We had another Expo at a big out-of-town shopping centre at Serpentine Green mid-month on a Friday evening, but surprisingly there were very few people about – probably because of the fine weather. Something that was said during the evening prompted me to do a bit more homework on the Athens course. I knew the Great North Run course, as I had already run it, and I also knew that the Peterborough course for the Great Eastern Run was already renowned in the running world for being a good course for Personal Best times as it was so incredibly flat. As Peterborough is on the edge of the Fens, the spiritual home of all flat earth types, then this just had to be true anyway, without even checking what roads they were to use. But Athens was a different kettle of fish completely. I'd never been there, but all the good tourist photos of Athens are dominated by big hills, and mountains all around, but it had never occurred to me that anyone would possibly organise a marathon route over anything other than a virtually flat course, or over the odd bridge or two. I realised I had broken my golden rule, and entered a race without checking the course first, but this one was different – this was THE COURSE, the authentic one, and it HAD TO BE DONE!

I got on to the race website, and immediately realised from the information pages that they had not been able to choose the course for this race, as it had been dictated by history! When I downloaded the course map and profile, I instantly realised why a number of runners I had spoken to had wished me luck but sworn that they would never do it. It also became quite plain why Phidippides had keeled over and died when he finished. A close inspection of the download revealed that there was effectively one stretch in the middle of the run which was uphill – one long uphill stretch that was FOURTEEN MILES LONG. It went from around mile 5 to around mile 19, but the route didn't give it all back in a nice equally downhill stretch, as the finish in Athens is higher above sea level than the start at Marathon. After I had caught my breath again, I realised that it would have made no difference if I had known before, I would still have entered as this was THE RACE. What I did do, however, was to immediately include hill runs in my training programme, and went looking for a suitable one, which was difficult to find in Fenland.

As it happens, I did find more or less the perfect little hill, very close to the gym, and just off one of my main favourite running routes. It was around 400 metres long, with a steady rise at a much steeper gradient than the Athens route, and was perfect for doing *hill reps*, run up, jog down, run up, jog down, always trying to beat the previous time. One session a week doing about 8 reps was substituted for an ordinary run, and I also tried to incorporate this little hill into longer Sunday runs. In my slightly quirky way, the hill from Milton Ferry Bridge up towards Castor became *Acropolis Hill*, at least until I actually walked up the real one on the Saturday before the race, anyway. It was murder on the quads, the big thigh muscles which took the brunt of running uphill, for the first few sessions, but they soon started to show the benefit. It also taught me a valuable lesson about understanding what you are letting yourself in for when you get carried away with new masterplans – however inspiring they may seem.

The month was rounded off with a photoshoot again, this time with Number Four, for *Chat* magazine. They wanted to do a piece on me, but from her perspective as most of their readers were ladies. The photographer was an American called Joe, who did a lot of these types of shoot, but was primarily a sports photographer. He had learned his trade photographing American Football in Florida and after that Saturday morning session with us he was heading off to a Premier League football match in London as his next assignment. We had a good gossip between shots, and he told me how he was hoping to get some work with Marathonfoto, who took the pictures of runners at some of the big events. I mentioned that I had actually arranged for them to come and do the photos for the Great Eastern Run, and we agreed that he would email me if he was on the team there.

September was an even quieter month than August had been. One Expo again, this time back in Queensgate where we had the first back in June. By now it was way too late for anyone to start preparing for the half marathon, so we were concentrating on the 5k fun run, but more on getting volunteers signed up to help organise the crowds on the day, and act as marshals. Alongside the committee made up from the local running clubs, and the City Council Sports Development Team, we would need about 350 volunteers on the day, or the runners could not run. There also had to be a significant turn out of the police, and paramedics, and first aid stations manned. By the end of the day we were just about there or thereabouts, and we had got a good few fun runners signed up too.

Number Four and Number Three's boyfriend were both just about ready for their first half marathon race. I had very deliberately not got too involved in trying to make sure that they had trained properly, as I really didn't want them to feel that I was in any way, shape or form creating pressure for them to do this run. I was fabulously excited at the prospect of them doing it, and knew that they would do well and enjoy themselves immensely, but I only wanted them to do it because they wanted to, not in any way because I wanted them to. We had quite a little party heading for Newcastle, or Whitley Bay which was where our hotel was located. We only wanted to stay one night, and none of the hotels near the centre of Newcastle would accept one night bookings that weekend, as they knew they could get all the business they wanted, and at ridiculously high prices too. Apart from me, all four girls were coming, and three boyfriends, so it was one car from Manchester for Number One, and two cars from Peterborough making the trek.

The party for Athens had grown a little too. The original plan was that the boys would come to Athens in November instead of going to Spain in October this year, although sadly a couple of them couldn't make it in November in the end. Luckily The Poseur, The Auld Git and Auld Thai Tam were able to make it, and were already all booked up. I had initially issued severe warnings about being on good behaviour before the race, so we had decided to head to Athens on the Thursday, spend Friday and Saturday *doing* Athens, Sunday would be the race, and on Monday we would head for the coast for the rest of the week and quite probably let our hair down a little, maybe. The Auld Git had been left in charge of finding and booking suitable hotels, and the plan was for them to fly down from Edinburgh to Gatwick and I would hook up with them at Gatwick from where we would fly down to Athens together. Numbers One and Two had by now decided to join us, and once I had cleared it with the boys (family were NEVER allowed near the boys' week normally) they had booked to come down from Friday to Monday, and found a hotel quite close to ours.

On the Monday before the Newcastle run, I had a session with my sports massage lady, Dorothy, a delightful and petite lady whose thumbs I once described on my blog as *having been forged in the furnaces of hell.* Luckily I didn't need to see her very often, as I always did my muscle stretching religiously; short stretches before a run, long stretches afterwards, and small stretches most days. However with such a long lay off, I wanted to be absolutely sure that everything was loose and in good shape before taking on two half marathons in eight days, so had booked for a leg massage to be on the safe side. I also always made sure there was a good few days between a sports massage and a race, as it could sometimes take a day or two to recover. There had been occasions when my calf muscles had got really tight, and the pain she inflicted then whilst getting all the knots out was unbelievable, but her hands were magic and she really knew her stuff well. After every session my legs always felt better than ever, so this session was as much about feeling good as it was about making sure it all worked well on the day.

On the Saturday we loaded into the cars and headed for Whitley Bay. I was driving Number Four and her boyfriend, and the others were coming in Number Two's car. We got there well ahead of the others, as Number Two is notoriously bad at getting going in the mornings , so I left the others to wait and once I had checked in I got the metro straight into Newcastle and headed for the Expo. This was one that we didn't need to attend to get race packs, which had all come in the post a couple of weeks before. It was also not a great Expo from the content and interest point of view, but there was always an excellent atmosphere, and most importantly it was the place where a number of bloggers would be hanging around for a meet up. In most cases it would be the only chance of meeting up, as the race was so huge and it was impossible to spot people in a crowd of 40,000 runners. I spent a great afternoon just sitting around chatting with running friends from the blogs, and mid way through the girls turned up for a look round as well as they had not seen the Expo last year as they only came for the race day itself.

Back at the Hotel in the evening we had dinner quite early for us, and of course played *spot the other runners* in the restaurant and bar. A late evening stroll along the rather windswept promenade just to make sure there were no cobwebs left, and then it was back to the room for the ritual *laying out of the race kit.* This year was going to be very different to last year's experience, and I was really looking forward to getting into the pens with the ordinary folk, and being part of that great running fraternity *up the back*. Last year had been a stunning experience, but this year I was looking forward to doing the *real world* thing. I was also a hell of a lot more relaxed because I knew the race, I knew the course, and I knew I could do it (even though I wasn't in quite as good shape (well running shape, that is) as last year bearing in mind the operations I'd had since then.

Great North Run Day, Sunday 5th October, dawned with a fine look to the weather, and after an early breakfast we kitted up and headed for the coaches to take us to the start. The others would be coming in later on the metro, but our package included transport so the running team went off to take full advantage. With everything that I had to go through the previous year once I arrived, I hadn't noticed that the coaches drop off their loads of runners incredibly early, because the coaches have to get off down to South Shields, or out of the area, before the roads are all closed. To make matters worse, with the others at the hotel we had been able to do without the hassle of the baggage buses, as our bags would be ready for us at the finish area courtesy of the support team – although we had promised to keep them light and in back packs! This all meant that we arrived at the start with absolutely ages to hang around doing very little except keep hydrated and try to keep warm and our muscles stretched.

Finally it was about time to wander down to the motorway itself and find our pens. These were just a simple method of keeping some semblance of order amongst such a huge number of runners at the start, and for the early part of the race. The theory was that you estimated your time for the race when you made your entry, and the fastest runners went towards the front, and the slower runners at the back, and you were split up into blocks of about 1000 runners *penned together* and each pen was released in turn. Number Three's boyfriend had estimated his time a bit faster than Number Four and I had, so he was allocated to a quicker, white pen whilst Number Four and I were luckily both in the same green pen, just a couple of pens back from him. The walk amongst the crowds from where we joined the motorway a couple of hundred yards after the start line took us up past the celebrity pen where I had been last year, and it occurred to me that I might just have got in there again with my security pass from last year if I had got lucky, but soon got over that thought. The walk on towards our pens was endless, and really brought home the immense size of the field of runners for this race. Any runner has the option of dropping back to start with other runners in a slower pen, but we knew that Number Three's boyfriend was keen to set himself a really good time for his first big race so we shoved him into his fast pen and kept going to find ours. We were determined to run a little way together, but I knew that soon enough she would probably leave me in her wake, and so she should, for goodness sake she was 36 years younger than me and if she couldn't run a bit faster than something was drastically wrong. In the end we were split up long before the actual start line was crossed, as when the pen was released I was stunned by how much of a rugby scrum it immediately became with folk elbowing and barging their way through as if there was clear open road 10 yards ahead. Little did they know that it was going to be crowded all the way to South Shields. I had been barged into the fence three times before I even got to cross the start, but nothing was going to spoil the day, so I kept smiling and got on with it.

The biggest difference I noticed from the previous year was that now that I was running at the slower end of the field, not only was it slightly more crowded, but there were far more people who had clearly no idea of any sort of race etiquette, and also who hadn't the first clue about pacing themselves. I spotted the support crew in the same place again on The Tyne Bridge, and got a shout and a high-5 as I ran by. Not long after the Tyne Bridge the route swung left onto the first short rise and I was staggered that we were temporarily brought to a virtual halt by the number of people *walking* up the rise after only about 3 miles. Not to worry, I started to weave my way along and was enjoying the atmosphere which was, to be fair, just a little bit more excited and fun-filled than the front of the race the previous year which had been slightly more about adrenaline and concentration.

As we hit the John Reid Road everything went just a little bit quieter as we started the long slight incline and I spotted one of those damned rhinos again. I think the WWF have had a few of these fantastic costumes made for their runners to wear at these events. They look huge, and are the shape of a giant rhino head, but are made of something extremely clever and weigh very little. However it doesn't do your ego any favours at all to find yourself getting beaten across the finish line by a bloody rhino, even if it is being worn by some super-hero runner. Come to think of it, anyone wearing one of those for a marathon, or *any* race, would be a super-hero in my eyes just to think of doing that feat. Yes, I admit that I was beaten by one in London, probably by more than one if the truth be known, but I got my own back in Edinburgh, and I wasn't going to be beaten again here, so found I had something to concentrate on for a while.

A few weeks before this race someone had been putting some photos up on their blog, and we discovered almost by accident that one of the bloggers from the North East, 'MTS', was my total double – we almost could have been twins separated at birth. It was an extraordinary likeness, and as soon as we realised that he was, as usual, going to be a marshal at the race and I was running it, we agreed to look out for each other. Now I know that this would normally be mission impossible to pick one runner out of 40,000, but I knew exactly where he would be stationed, just past the water station around 11 miles, and he had helped matters by fixing up a Realbuzz sign on a pole so that all the bloggers running would look out and shout a "Hi" to him. As soon as I spotted the sign I homed in on it, and as my time was shot to pieces by the crowds of *ramblers* and *hill-walkers* I stopped for a chat and to get some pictures for the blog of the two of us together.

A minute or two later I was dropping down the hill onto The Leas with the final mile to the finish, so tried to pick up the pace and salvage a few more seconds. As I crossed the line the Red Arrows were just finishing their display, and there was a huge vapour trail heart in the sky over South Shields, which just about summed it all up. I grabbed a water bottle, and a goodie bag and medal, and wandered across the muddy field towards the T-shirt pick-up points, which were signposted Small, Medium, Large and X-Large. I was now on fully knackered auto pilot, but headed for the X-Large queue as despite all the weight loss I knew that I needed an XL T-shirt as they were always a bit small and I had a broad chest. However, when under a bit of stress its weird how the brain *reverts to base*. There were still times when it was clear that my subconscious still wasn't fully re-programmed to the new conditions, and this was one of them. As I joined the queue for the shirts, a very tall and wide guy in front of me asked me if they had any super-sized shirts, and the marshal there told him to go round to the last box where they had the really big ones. Naturally, he had saved me the bother of asking so I followed the habits of a lifetime and went round to the last box for a super-sized, tucked it into my goodie bag and headed for the Charity Village for the reunion.

When I got to The Prostate Cancer Charity tent the gang were all there, and we very soon got the text messages from the chip timing computer system with our finish times. Mine was 2 hours 32 minutes 16 seconds, only 8 minutes slower than last year which, given the crowds, the stop off for a chat with MTS and the operation, wasn't too bad an effort. Number Four had clocked a brilliant 2 hours 12 minutes 51 seconds, and solidly beaten my time of last year in the process. The star was Number Three's boyfriend who had set the wonderful time of 1 hr 51 minutes 34 seconds, and who was convinced that in a less crowded race could have knocked loads off that time. If he decides to stick with it, he has the potential to become a very creditable runner indeed. The next hour passed by in pretty much of a blur, grabbing the odd sandwich, having photos taken, meeting other Prostate Cancer runners and staff, and some of the other bloggers who were running dropped by as they knew exactly where I would be. Then it was time for the long trek to the coach pick-up, and the interminably delayed trip back to the hotel which we didn't reach till about 6 o'clock.

Our hotel were very generous in letting us use one of the rooms to shower and change bearing in mind that we had technically checked out hours ago, so we were suitably refreshed before we hit the road south again. To be honest, the roads had their moments that night, but it wasn't too bad and, even with a stop off at Wetherby services where we actually met up with the other car, we were home by midnight and deciding the washing machine could wait till the morning!

With another visit to Dorothy on the Tuesday, just to be on the safe side with another race the following Sunday, the rest of that week was taken up with last minute preparations for Number Four's imminent departure to York University to read Philosophy. Originally we had thought that she would move in to the halls of residence there on the

Saturday, but they had now changed it to the Sunday, clashing with the Great Eastern Run which I couldn't miss now as Ambassador. Number Two had instantly offered to drive her up, and I was sure that her help and advice would be an improvement on mine anyway as she had already been to University herself and knew the ropes from the student viewpoint, which I certainly didn't. During the week I got an email from Joe, the photographer, confirming that he was indeed on the photography team for the race, and trying to beg a car parking spot, but by then he was out of luck.

By Saturday I was getting quite excited as all around the City the signage was going up for the race, and the start and finish area equipment was being installed. I had a relaxed day meeting up with bloggers as they arrived in the city, and had a really good chat over lunch with Shazzoah from Lancashire and her son who was keeping her company for the weekend. She had run the Great North Run last week, and was not doing the race here, but had come all the way from north of Manchester just to volunteer as a marshal as it was my race. This was typical of the amazing community we had built up over the previous year or so, on the blog site, and it was fantastic to meet her for the first time.

Later that evening I had arranged for a small gathering of bloggers and their families who were staying overnight before the race to meet up for dinner at my health club, and about a dozen of us had a great time meeting up and getting to know each other a bit better. They were a little reticent at first about my theory, established with Angie K the night before the London Marathon, that a little red wine the night before a race was a good thing, but they didn't put up much of a fight in all honesty and the evening was a great success.

Race morning dawned and it was terrific to be able to get kitted up at home and then just stroll out of the door 10 minutes before I was needed. This more or less coincided with the arrival of Jach222 from Northampton, another blogger who was coming over to marshal and who had bagged one of my car parking spaces early in the planning stage. I had to move on though, as I had been warned that I might be required for some radio interviews early on. When I arrived in Cathedral Square the place was beginning to buzz, and the race director was going through the final check list so that he could officially sign everything off and declare the race a 'go'! I was immediately intercepted and introduced to Iwan Thomas, who was appearing as the official starter of the race. This was another of my sporting heroes, a guy who had represented us winning Olympic medals, and was the British record holder at his event – the 400 metres. He was very relaxed, and a lot of fun, and took a great deal of interest in my story. Once we had done a couple of radio interviews he was kind enough to allow me to get a photo or two with him, then was happy for me to drag him around the square introducing him to various bloggers and friends I spotted in the crowds and having endless photos taken with all of them. Mind you, he very deliberately got his own back in style when the time came for him to get up on the stage in front of all the assembled runners for the official warm up exercise routine led by a personal trainer from my gym. He absolutely insisted that as he had willingly gone everywhere with me, it was now my turn to go with him. That was NOT funny!

Minutes later he was dragged away to the starter's rostrum, and I slipped quietly into the crowd of runners and we were off. To say it was strange running amongst 4000 people along streets I normally drove down every day was an understatement. But it was enormous fun, and it was also a great feeling knowing that there were NO hills of any kind to have to deal with. The way my legs felt after the half marathon the week before I'm not entirely certain how I would have fared if we had been faced with any serious inclines. As we jogged merrily along I was particularly struck by the number of people who were lining the streets and cheering on the runners, and there was even a few bands along the way lifting our spirits. The weather became unseasonably hot for an English October, and kind folk along the way had set up their own impromptu water stations for thirsty runners.

I have just a few abiding memories of that race. The *fun* ones were when I reached a point about a mile from the finish and spotted Shazzoah and Jach222 marshalling away at adjacent road junctions. In the heat, and that far into the race, I was pretty well soaked to the skin in sweat and not something you would want to get too familiar with – but I'm sorry to say that in a sudden fit of mischievousness I managed to give each of them a huge enveloping great hug! They were still uttering good natured expletives when we met up again after the finish – at least I assumed they were good natured. A little further on as we passed through the last terraces of houses I took a short walk break and an old couple standing on their doorstep tried to lift my spirits and urged me to get to the finish. My explanation of taking a quick breather so that I could do a photogenic sprint finish left them chuckling as I headed on. The other fun memory was when I was approaching the final turn into the finish area, and saw Joe on photo duty there. He had been looking out for me, and was jumping up and down and yelling at me, then completely ignored the other runners around me and tried to break the world record for the largest number of photos taken in the shortest time as I passed him with a wave and a grin.

The best memory of all was a much deeper affair, and one that will stay with me for a very long time. About 8 miles into the race I was plodding along minding my own business and enjoying the whole friendly atmosphere surrounding the day. I realised as I jogged along that I had somehow seemed to pick up a number of runners who were in close formation behind me, and who, for want of a better explanation, seemed to be deliberately running with me. After a while I asked if everyone was all right and enjoying themselves, and got strong affirmative responses, even if some of them looked as though they had had better days. One of the guys then said to me:

"I hope you don't mind me running with you. I only entered this race because of you, and I've never done anything like this before. When I saw you come past I just wanted to be able to say that I had run with you on the race."

The others more or less said the same thing. I really did not know what on earth to say in reply. This was uncharted territory from a different planet. What on earth was I supposed to say? I had no idea, so I just said something like:

"You're more than welcome, and it's a pleasure to run with you guys."

I wouldn't exactly want to suggest that I was *welling up* or anything like that, as I don't tend to do that sort of stuff, but it was a really emotional moment, and it made me feel so good about myself in a way that I hadn't felt before. These were a bunch of ordinary folk, out on a Sunday doing something extraordinary which may well enhance their lives and self respect more than they could realise. And they were doing it because of me? That was stunning.

As I crossed the finish line in what I later found to be 2 hours 29 minutes 05 seconds the announcer spotted me coming and was giving me quite a reception on the PA system, but at that point I just wanted to get a water bottle and my medal and T-shirt and have a lie down in the sun. Unfortunately I had been instructed to show my face in the VIP tent when I finished, but as no one had supplied me with a pass I had the devils own job getting past security and was only finally admitted when one of the council people came by and vouched for me. I shook a few hands, grabbed a drink and some sandwiches, then made my excuses and left to join the crowd of bloggers and supporters who by now were sunbathing outside the Prostate Cancer Charity stand. Soon enough it was time for folk to start their long journeys home, but *Pam* and *Chris*, a blogging couple from Manchester were staying over for the extra night, and I had arranged the evening schedule for them. I took them out to the country park where I did all my training runs; then we popped to my gym for a wonderfully relaxing session in the steam room and Jacuzzi before heading to my favourite floating Chinese restaurant on the river to round things off.

When I came to *report* the day on my blog I remember trying to sum up how I felt. My final comment on the day was

"To call my expression tonight SMILING would be akin to referring to the Sistine Chapel as having a nice picture on the ceiling."

CHAPTER TWENTY-ONE

A NEW BEGINNING

BY NOW ATHENS WAS DOMINATING ALL MY THOUGHT PROCESSES, AND THE challenge that it was going to present. As a result of the publicity campaign that Realbuzz had involved me in during the summer, and probably because they had put a write-up about me and a link to my blog on their home page, I was currently receiving over 1000 visits a day to my blog, and the support I was getting because of this was tremendous. I couldn't wait to get out there, and I had been soaking up all the information on the website like a sponge. My sense of history was in full overdrive, and I was sublimely convinced that this race was certainly the best possible marathon to run. It was nowhere near as big as the *World Majors* in London, New York, Boston, Chicago and Berlin, or even as big of some of the others like Rome and Paris, but this was probably as much down to its extremely tough course, and even maybe to its location as well.

Just to take my mind off it, I had one more appointment with Mr Gillespie coming up at the end of October, when I hoped he would sign me off for good. When I got in to see him he had one more go at getting anything out of the now very small swellings without much success, and declared himself satisfied with the healing process. He also took the chance to tell me about his Jungfrau Marathon in September, in return for my tales about my two half marathons. He had not really been aware of the Great Eastern Run, but told me that he would look out for it and do it himself next year.

Then he asked me to undress down to my underpants, put my arms out, and "Give me a twirl". I did as I was bidden wondering what on earth he was up to, and the nurse in attendance looked a little bemused too:

"Damn it. There's absolutely nothing else I can possibly do to improve anything."

He had been reluctant to let me go, and was actually checking to see if there was any other loose bits anywhere that he could work his magic on. He told me that not only had he never seen anyone lose so much weight the way I had, just by diet and exercise, but that he had never seen anyone work so successfully to make sure everything ended up well toned – no bingo wings, no saggy jowls or neck wrinkles. Nothing he could possibly work on. Sadly he told me he would place me on his *SOS list*, which he explained meant that if I ever wanted to talk to him about anything to do with medical matters relating to reconstructive surgery I wouldn't need to go through the usual channels with my doctor referring me, but that his secretary would have me on his special list and all I had to do was phone him.

This was the most wonderful news I could possibly have had a week before going to Athens. Four years and 2½ weeks after the car crash I now had an *organism* that the top reconstructive surgery team at one of the top hospitals in the country couldn't improve upon. I felt totally elated, and unbelievably proud of myself. It wasn't just a case of *who would have believed it*, it was a full blown case of *I wouldn't have believed it* back then.

Almost naturally now, I took one final precaution before catching the flight – I let Dorothy loose on my legs again *just to be sure*. Then on the Thursday it was off to Gatwick to find the boys in a bar there moaning about the price of drinks in airports, but seriously ready for a good trip. I managed to impress upon them the high importance I placed on being fit and ready for the race on Sunday, and to give them their due they behaved impeccably for as long as it was required.

The plan was to spend the Friday getting our bearings, and going to the Expo to pick up my race pack, number, chip and goodie bag so that we would be free on the Saturday to do the sights with the girls who didn't arrive till Friday evening. The Expo was in a conference and exhibition centre with the grandest of entrances that only the Greeks could do with such style, all marble and looking like a massive old temple. Unfortunately we only discovered that later as we had managed to find our way to it via the back door, which was significantly less than impressive. We played who can acquire the most *baseball caps*, *stress balls and bananas* for a while, then once I had registered and got all the necessary paperwork I got very slightly carried away and bought some great T-shirts with various designs around the race, especially for use in the gym when I got home. As usual there was a *wall* for sticking up messages about anything you wanted to say about the race, and whereas I normally pass these by, I decided I wanted to put one up this time. Nothing fancy, or emotional, just my personal mantra for runs of this magnitude:

"It's not the time – it's crossing the line."

I would never be a fast runner, but running these races wasn't about beating anyone or anything but my own expectations of myself. Talking of which I had made known my target for this race on my blog before taking off. Bearing in mind that I had done London in 5:46:05, and Edinburgh in 5:54:57, and these were both relatively flat courses, I had given considerable thought as to what I should aim for here, especially as I was *going public* on it on the blog and didn't like reporting missed targets without a plausible excuse. The race itself had a 6 hour target time, which meant that the *sweep up* bus would track the route picking up stragglers and those injured at exactly the speed it takes to complete the course in 6 hours, and although you were under no obligation to get on the bus if it passed you they would be reopening the roads to traffic behind the bus and if you were overtaken you had to stick to the pavements from then on. There would be the added complication that all water stations, energy drink stations, and first aid posts would also close down as the sweep-up bus passed them. This race had a 14 mile uphill section in it, which warranted serious consideration in target setting, but nevertheless I wouldn't be entirely happy with myself if I didn't beat the bus back to the finish, so I had set my official, public target as 6 hours exactly, with my heart in my mouth when I did so.

Once we got out of the Expo, this time via the front door and saw how spectacular it was, we got some *team* photos, and then suddenly spotted the Acropolis just through some trees. We also noticed that there were all sorts of historic things all around, with the Temple of Zeus a couple of hundred yards down the approach, and the Panathinaikon Stadium just away to our left. First things first though, as we had spotted a good looking alfresco bar about 50 yards away. It transpired that they served excellent cold beer and hot pizza, even though after a short while they rapidly switched to hot beer and cold pizza if you didn't get on with it. Duly refuelled we headed down the way to look at the Temple of Zeus (we only discovered that was what the impressive marble columns actually were when we got there at five past three and read the sign on the gate, although we hadn't bargained on the smaller sign underneath announcing that it shut at three).

Undaunted by this set back, we gave it the once-over through the fence, and duly decided that it was probably best viewed from a little distance anyway or we might get sore necks. We headed back up towards the Parliament Building and then onwards towards the hotel, but to be honest the air quality in Athens is pretty diabolical and by now we were ready for a quiet little relaxation somewhere while we waited for the girls to arrive when we could find a good spot for dinner.

Saturday was a great day, but by the evening I realised that it had been a lousy way to prepare for a marathon the next day. We had started off joining forces with the girls at our hotel, and then had simply walked in the general direction of the Acropolis on the basis that it was probably too big to miss. We worked our way past the edge of the flea market and found a *road train* – the sort of train on ordinary wheels, not tracks, you normally find running around theme parks, or along promenades – which took us halfway up the hill, and completed the rest of the climb on foot. The Parthenon and the other temples around there, and the theatres along the side of the hill are without doubt some of the most awe inspiring sites I have ever had the privilege to visit. The view from the top of the hill is a 360° panorama of Athens, and I couldn't help myself but try to work out the route I would be taking the next day, and try to capture a bird's eye view of it. Looking at the hills surrounding Athens I sincerely hoped my geography was wrong! Once we had hitched a ride part of the way back with the next road train, I couldn't help but drag everyone round to the Panathinaikon Stadium for a proper look at where the race would finish. A lot of the barriers were already up, and feverish activity was under way with all the preparations, but this was truly a magnificent sight. It was rebuilt as the stadium for the first modern Olympic Games in 1896, and is a classic u-shaped, open ended stadium seating 80,000 people and built entirely of marble. The five rings, iconic symbol of the Olympic Games, still proudly dominate the skyline above the stadium, and I could almost feel the power of the track there. The race route ran into the stadium, up onto the track, and finished at the far end, and I memorised that image ready for when I would really need it the next day.

By now it was very late in the afternoon, and it suddenly occurred to me that my usual careful fuelling strategy had gone right out of the window, as we hadn't actually stopped anywhere for a meal all day. I simply had to get something to eat, and we ended up in a souvlaki bar just round the corner from the hotel experiencing Greek chicken and chips (I know – terrible thing to eat before a race, but so much better than nothing at that point in the day). Once back at the hotel we got a shower and a change, and planned to meet up to go out for dinner somewhere that I could get a decent bowl of pasta. While getting suitable directions from reception, I also asked about a good Indian restaurant for the next night. This might be Athens, but by now it was part of my rule book – an Indian meal after a marathon was essential, and I knew that all the rest of the crew liked Indian food so we just had to find one.

After a short stroll we pitched up at an obviously popular local hostelry to get dinner, and my bowl of pasta. Unfortunately time appears to stand still in Saturday night restaurants the world over, and this was a prime example of that phenomenon. It took absolutely hours to get seated, place our orders and eventually get served, by which time I was in two minds whether to bother. When the food arrived I just tucked straight in, got it down as fast as sensibly possibly, made my excuses and left the others to enjoy the rest of their night while I went straight back to the hotel, laid out my kit and hit the sack just after midnight. When it comes to preparation for a marathon, the day had been utter madness, an absolute classic of ineptitude, bearing in mind that I had to be up at about 5 o'clock. I was sharing with Auld Thai Tam, and I had left him with the absolute certainty that he would suffer irreparable damage to certain more sensitive parts of his anatomy if he either disturbed any of my kit laid out, or disturbed me, when he eventually arrived back. To his eternal credit he did neither, and he was still peacefully dreaming when I headed down for a light breakfast in the morning.

I was surprised to see quite so many runners in the breakfast room, but it turned out that one of the inclusive package deals was based here. When

I had got kitted up and headed out about 6:30 they were all gathering in the lobby and being ticked off on a list before boarding a coach. I decided that rather than experiment with the metro I would stretch my legs with a walk down to the stadium where we had to report by 7 o'clock. When I arrived there, a huge, but fast-moving, queue had already developed, and I quickly discovered that it comprised runners from all over the world in a magnificent multi-cultural adrenaline soup. The town of Marathon, site of the original Battlefield and where the race started, had no direct public transport links with Athens, so the organisers, with whistle blowing efficiency, transported the entire field there by coach, and then once they had transported the runners, they also took any spectators out there free as well. My crew were going to do just that, and had planned to get to the stadium about an hour after me.

As my part of the queue approached the coach line and the whistle blowing got louder and louder, I found myself swept up in a group of Belgians resplendent in matching Médecins sans Frontières track suits and looking great, even if I couldn't understand a word of their excited chat. On the coach I found myself sat next to a Greek runner but once we had exhausted the sign language exchange covering the fact, I think, that this was his first marathon and my third (or perhaps he had one child, who knows?), and he discovered another Greek guy sitting across the aisle, I settled down to the view of the course that we would inevitably get on the drive out to Marathon. Actually I ended up dozing off for a while; I must have looked really relaxed! The bits of the road I did see were totally daunting anyway, so I contented myself with the suggestion that they were probably taking us a different way via a shortcut the coach drivers knew. Naive or what?

Arriving at Marathon we got off the coach to be greeted by some young volunteers handing out large clear bin liners to everyone as they stepped down to the road. This was a thoughtful touch indeed, as we had probably got a little too comfortable on the coach and it was still quite chilly out there. Banks of portaloos were lined up on the edge of a piece of rough ground, and there were a few straggly bushes about for the men, too. Basic, but most practical, and nobody seems to mind if it relieves the stress of the moment.

I followed the general trend across the main road where we had been set down and up a broad side street to where the baggage lorries were waiting, in a large car park, each one marked up with a section of running numbers ready to receive our Athens Marathon plastic kitbags with number duly stuck on the side. Water bottles were freely available everywhere you looked. I sorted myself out, dumped off my bag and followed the flow further up the road to what turned out to be the small marathon stadium running track with banked seating all round. A lot of runners were warming up on the track, but I reasoned that this was a day for conserving as much energy as possible, and I would use the first mile or two in the crowd as my main warm up rather than waste any by running anywhere before the starting gun. Small children were weaving amongst the crowds of runners handing out tiny olive branches to every runner, which was a genuine delight, and such a great gesture by the organisers. By now I was beginning to think that whoever was responsible for managing this event was a total professional, as everything seemed to have been thought of from the runners' perspective, with the emphasis on safety, comfort and enjoying the experience.

As I wandered along soaking up the atmosphere I heard my name shouted out, and realised the crew had arrived and spotted me. None of them had actually seen the start of a race like this, and I think at that point we were all pretty excited. Then we spotted something I had been looking for as I had walked towards the start area. There on a plinth, at the top of a flight of steps, just behind the start line, was that most potent symbol of all, the Olympic Flame. It had been brought by the historic torch relay to Marathon on Saturday lunchtime and would remain lit till we had departed for Athens. There was just no need to say anything, standing there, waiting for the start, with the Olympic Flame burning brightly high above the runners. What a moment!

Someone started saying something over the PA system, but it was all Greek to me (sorry, that had to be said at some stage, and at least it's out of the way now!). As they chatted, an American lady runner and a friend she had just made from London looked at me and started chuckling to themselves. One of the *extra touches* the organisers had thrown in was putting your name clearly on the bottom of your bib number, and they had obviously been struck by the fact that my name was Hare, which they thought most appropriate for a runner. I tried to make them understand that something had been lost in translation and it should have read tortoise, but they refused to believe me, especially when they got out of me that it was my third marathon of the year. This little bit of banter passed those nervous few moments before the gun, which almost took us by surprise as we hadn't understood what was being said. I had one last look around Marathon Stadium, the sky was clear and TV helicopters hovered overhead, it was not too warm, forecast to be around 18 degrees with only a light breeze off the sea. The gun went off, and we shuffled forward, walked forward, jogged forward, then there it was – that familiar whine of the computer sensors reacting to all the timing chips attached to running shoes as we passed through the *Start* arch to the accompaniment of cheers from the supporters; we were off.

This one didn't feel like the others. There was an extra something you could almost feel it in the air, and it looked as though most runners were aware of it as we started the run to Athens. The course quietly wandered along a fairly open, more or less flat, road for the first 2½ miles or so, and then we took a very sharp turn left up a side road with runners coming back towards us on the other side of the road. There was quite a crowd of supporters at the junction, with coaches at the ready behind them for the trip back to Athens to watch the finish a bit later on. This little section off the main road was the single most important part of the course. We ran for a few hundred metres through the sweetest-smelling orange groves literally dripping with ripe fruit, and then the route slowly circled its way around the Marathon Battlefield where the Greek Army had defeated the invading Persians. There in the centre of the Battlefield was the mass grave mound where they had buried the 180 fallen Greek Heroes, and in front of it the flame burning in a small memorial.

Now we were definitely running in the original footsteps of Phidippides 2,498 years ago, and what a privilege to be allowed to honour his story in such a tangible way. The course returned back onto the main road to Athens – Marathon Avenue, and the field slowly strung itself out more and more as we passed through villages along the way, amid knots of supporters and spectators from whom the international cry of support needed no translation for any of us, wherever we were from:

"Bravo."

Just after mile 7 or so, the road started to climb gently towards the hills. Here we go, I thought, and battened down the mental hatches as this hill would last for nearly 14 miles and over that distance rise around 1000 feet. This would be the equivalent of running an entire half marathon, and a bit more for good measure, on an incline of about 3%, but I banished such thoughts. As far as I was concerned it was just going to be a short hill that only lasted until the next bend, and was therefore not a problem. Once round that bend, we had another short hill section just as far as that little village up ahead, which wasn't that far in real terms. And so it went on, just a consecutive series of short hills, each one perfectly manageable in its own way. There were water stations every 2½ kilometres, energy drink stations every 5k, they even had the odd energy gel station, and banana station. First Aid posts were dotted along the course, and there were toilet blocks alongside every water station, and sponge stations now and again just so that you didn't have to waste a bottle of water tipping it over your head. It was just as though the organisers were acutely aware of how tough this was, and they would do anything in their power to help us to succeed and stay in reasonable shape. Everything was going fairly well, and although I wasn't travelling too quickly I *was* travelling. At about the 20k mark (nearly 13 miles in), just before half way, I had to take a rapid toilet break and was heartened to see that because of their abundant supply there was no queue. In short order I was back on the road and forging along in my own sweet way.

Then I became aware of some sort of PA system and some bloke chattering excitedly away, but didn't take too much notice as I couldn't understand a word of it. But it went on and on, and seemed to be getting very loud and close behind me. On runs like these my rule is *never look back*, but it seemed necessary to break it at this turn of events, and to my utter dismay I discovered it was the *sweep up* convoy, with the course director exhorting runners to get on the bus as it passed them as the road would be reopened to traffic right behind the bus. At this point I realised that I had paused my Garmin inadvertently at some stage, and all my calculations of time and overall pace were completely up the spout. Even so, I reckoned the sweeper was slightly ahead of schedule, but not by that much so I couldn't argue.

My target was to beat the bus to the finish, so I dug in and tried to keep ahead of it but the constant uphill was by now wreaking havoc with my quads, however well I had prepared them. The whole organism started whingeing and whining fit to bust, and to make matters worse the lead car of the sweeper convoy had now driven up alongside me and the guy was trying to tell me something. I made the international *face* for I don't understand you, and he switched to fluent English to exhort me to get on the bus or I would be on my own, and on the pavement.

The devil in the back of my head began making a rapid list:

We don't know the way from here to the finish without marshals and roads closed, and they will take down the signs as soon as the bus passes by.

We're still only half way there.

These hills go on for miles yet.

There will be no more water stations

There will be no more first aid posts

There will be no further chance to get on the bus when it passes

We'll be on our own, knackered, no money...

The worst thing about it was that I knew perfectly well, (Spock would have called it "entirely logical"), that it would actually be foolhardy not to get on the bus, it was the only sensible option, and at that point I actually found myself checking to see how full the first one was.

That was the low point, about as deep as I could sink without actually going under. This was a place I hadn't been to before in a long time – failure. Certainly my first failure since I began this project. As I plodded along beside that car, I was staring defeat in the face and it was NOT a pretty sight. The voice in my head was screaming

"GET ON THE BUS – we can't take the risk, at least we tried."

"NO WAY, AM I QUITTER?" I screamed back, and then wondered how on earth I could possibly get to the end without water and all that stuff.

The answer was simple, stay ahead of the bus!

By now the car had gone on ahead and he was shouting at some runners up ahead as he had shouted at me. Don't blame him, I thought, it's just his job today. But the bus was alongside me now and it was now or never, the chips were down, *a defining moment.*

I let it go, and my game plan now was to try to keep it in sight as long as I could while we were still on the hills and then try to get it back again when the course flattened out a bit into Athens. For the next kilometre or so I could still see it way up ahead now, but it didn't seem to be getting any further away, and I started to focus on it to the exclusion of all else. I slowly but surely started to gain on it and grind it down, until around the 26 kilometre mark I overtook the bloody thing (it was by now a very personal battle between me and that bus). I even got past the car again very slowly, and got a huge smile from the guy doing the shouting as I gave him a thumbs-up and a crooked grin.

Next in my sights were a small group of five American runners who were wasting way too much breath, chatting as I passed them. But over the next few kilometres I have no idea what the route was like, what the scenery was like, how many spectators were around (although I vaguely recollect a smattering of bravo's and a band playing). I had become focussed completely and utterly, as you do sometimes in situations like that, on an pair of exceptionally long, well tanned and very feminine legs emanating extremely high up from a very close fitting pair of brown shorts which just happened to be running at exactly the same pace as me at that point. Well sometimes you just have to take inspiration and motivation from wherever you can find it, and I'm certain I was neither the first or last gentleman runner to be inspired in the presence of lycra shorts.

Regrettably the legs ahead began to waver on the continuous climb, and I was forced to play the cad and overtake them, leaving them to their fate on that country road. I did have the decency to mentally concede that it was extremely unlikely that she would find an equivalent level of inspiration from our reversed positions, so had the good grace to move on as fast as I could to save her from undue suffering on that count. Even in such inspired mode, I was still only just ahead of the convoy, which had clearly decided to play cat and mouse with me. There was now only a couple more kilometres of climb left before we would flatten off and actually get some downhill bits, and I had to let the convoy go past this time without further discussion. I promised the guy in the car that I would get him back when the road flattened, but I doubt that he was either aware of, or bothered by my muttered threats.

I concentrated now on keeping a couple of runners in sight ahead, to know where to go if the road re-opened in front of me. Luckily the re-opening wasn't very efficient and never actually caught up with me. The convoy was still visible on straighter sections, and although the water stations were busily closing down they were still looking out for runners and making sure we were catered for. At the 32 kilometre mark the hill finally gave up torturing us and flat road has never felt so sensually gratifying before, and probably never will again. Flat road meant a release of tensions throughout my body, and my quads burst into song with the sheer pleasure of only having to do ordinary running now. I was back in the game, and caught myself smiling broadly at anyone still standing along the roadside shouting bravos.

I was getting a whole new buzz from somewhere, and knew from my Garmin that I was actually picking up the pace again. I mentally clicked into my own special mode for the last stages of races, starting to actually target runners in view ahead. No longer were they signposts for the route, now they were the next person I would overtake, and before long I was picking them off in surprised ones and twos as we entered the outskirts of Athens proper. The course still had one or two sneaky little surprises for us, short sharp rises here and there, and the ghastly down and up slopes of motorway underpasses, but on the whole I was used to these from my repetitions up *Acropolis Hill* during the last few months. They proved to be a very good hunting ground for overtaking the odd suffering soul, but I knew what it could be like and shouted a little encouragement to each as I passed them.

About 37 kilometres I spotted the bus again in the distance, and that was just the final impetus that I needed. I was going to have that bus! My target was to beat 6 hours, and the bus was on 6 hour pace, and I had told my girls I would be there in 6 hours and I didn't want them worrying. That bus was mine the moment I saw it again and it couldn't cheat by throwing hills at me any more. By 38k I was past the bus and taking the lead car in front of it with a punch of the air from me and a smile and a shout from Mr Megaphone. Central Athens tried to throw a few little hills into my path, but these were pathetic little hills now that I brushed aside with the disdain they deserved. By 40k I was getting *that feeling* again with only 2k or so to go. The feeling you get when you have been battling for over five hours on the edge of physical ability, when you are pretty much a spent force, and running on guts alone, but when you realise that you have the finish within your grasp, and absolutely know for certain that you ARE going to cross that finish line.

41k, the crowds are pretty much made up of finished runners heading home, but giving you the sort of encouragement that comes from their own recent experience of what you are going through and seems special because of it. By now I was getting that *finishing straight* feeling I had felt before, but very strongly this time. It's the point at which you can throw caution to the wind and give it absolutely everything you've got left because there is no longer any reason to hold anything back – there are no *later stages* left. I actually dredged the reserves, picked up the pace, and overtook a couple more runners before turning sharp left and down the slope of some sort of tree lined avenue, with glimpses of huge houses, even saw one with guards in national costume standing outside from the corner of my eye. On down the slope I picked up speed a little bit more and was feeling fabulous as I came through some gates at the bottom and straight out across the big dual carriageway and realised I was about to run into the Panathinaikon Stadium.

WHAT A SIGHT!

Crowds of finished runners gave a good cheer as I ran up across the pavement, I heard The Poseur shouting but couldn't see him, the course closed in to a narrow gap through a funnel of fenced crowds on both sides, suddenly it widened again and I looked up to see the Olympic Rings above the stadium where I was running on that historic track, towards the finish line with my arms raised, and my girls yelling from the track side.

5 hours 58 minutes 57 seconds. Yes, I beat my target!

I AM A REAL AUTHENTIC MARATHON RUNNER.

As they say in Athens (and on one of my T-shirts) I have run THE AUTHENTIC.

The races in London and Edinburgh had been tough, but they were relatively easy courses, (apart from the distance). This race had used a fourteen mile hill to bring me face to face with failure.

It was, and will forever remain, a defining moment in every way.

During that race I had learnt what it is really like to dig deep into dark recesses and take on my demons in hand to hand combat, back them down, and discover for the first time that I have what it takes to complete the biggest challenge I have ever attempted.

The surgeon had finally given me confirmation that I had won the battle over my physical self in the week before I took off for Athens. In Athens I had finally confirmed that I had won the battle over my mental self, but the strangest thing of all is that I had never realised that I was even in that battle, or that it was the most important part of the project, until I had won it.

I have no idea what the future holds; that's what makes life such an adventure now. What I do know for sure is that it is going to be a totally different story, as it now has the benefit of a completely new central character.